With an Ear to the Ground

Essays on Sustainable Agriculture
1997 to 2003

by Vern Grubinger

Northeast Region
Sustainable Agriculture Research and Education
Burlington, Vermont

About the author. Vern Grubinger is a carbon-based organism, fueled primarily by fermented and caffeinated beverages, who works to enhance the interface between the photosynthetic and human communities. He works for the University of Vermont Cooperative Extension program as their vegetable and berry specialist, and is the director of the University of Vermont Center for Sustainable Agriculture. He also tries to coach first grade basketball and swims a lot of laps in pursuit of endorphins.

Northeast Region Sustainable Agriculture Research and Education
April 2004
All rights reserved
Printed in Canada

ISBN: 1-888626-08-9

Grubinger, Vernon P.
    With an Ear to the Ground: Essays on Sustainable Agriculture, 1997 to 2003.
Edited and with an introduction by Helen Husher.
        1. Sustainable agriculture. 2. Vermont—agriculture. 3. Vermont—quality of life.
4. Vermont Public Radio.

Except for "Reduce Risk by Buying Local Food," all the essays in this book were originally developed for Vermont Public Radio. They appear here with titles and in a slightly altered form to accommodate the difference between broadcast and print.

Cover illustration by Bonnie Acker
Cover design by Futura Design
Interior design by Andrea Gray

Northeast SARE
10 Hills Building
105 Carrigan Drive
University of Vermont
Burlington, VT 05405-0082
www.uvm.edu/~nesare

Contents

2002

2003

Acknowledgements

I'd first like to thank Ethan Allen and the Green Mountain Boys for starting the Republic of Vermont, where I have been blessed to find gainful employment and a wonderful place to raise a family.

Speaking of which, my wife and children deserve credit for putting up with me and going along willingly, for the most part, with my warped sense of humor. The kids provided me with plenty of radio commentary substrate, and they were too young to be upset about it.

My sincere gratitude goes to Vermont Public Radio for giving me a platform to mouth off big time. Betty Smith, commentary editor extraordinaire, helped me learn to speak in three-minute sound bites. She also urged me to be entertaining enough to limit the number of radios turning off simultaneously to fewer than several thousand statewide. I'll never forget the first time I taped a commentary in the studio with her. "You know," she said kindly afterward, "it's not a lecture."

Thank you to Frank Sands and family for hooking me up with VPR, for hosting its Norwich studio, and for your steady support of the UVM Center for Sustainable Agriculture.

My appreciation to University of Vermont Extension for (a) hiring me, (b) not firing me, (c) giving me several different jobs at once, and (d) allowing me the freedom to do those jobs as I see fit. And to my stakeholders and beneficiaries, formerly known as farmers and the public, thanks for working with me to both seek and provide knowledge as I struggle to fulfill extension's mission to improve the quality of life with information.

Kudos to Northeast Sustainable Agriculture Research and Education (SARE) for being progressive but not alienating mainstream farmers, for continually innovating with their grant programs, and for facilitating real change (however slow but steady) in our food and farming system. Fred Magdoff deserves a lot of the credit for providing the leadership to make these things happen. And thanks also for wanting to publish this book.

Helen Husher at Northeast SARE was instrumental in getting this book done, and is largely responsible for anything about it that you may like.

Finally, my thanks go to all the authors, farmers, web sites, magazines, and other sources of information that I may have shamelessly used without giving proper credit—such is the nature of radio. Since I was only allotted a few hundred words per commentary, some things had to be left unsaid.

— V. G.

With an Ear to the Ground

Essays on Sustainable Agriculture
1997 to 2003

Introduction

Not long ago, the Midwest Sustainable Agriculture Working Group looked at the results of focus groups and surveys from around the country to see how farmers and consumers think and talk about the issues facing agriculture. One of the things they learned was that the slogans "farm crisis," "rural crisis," and "save the family farm" are actually not all that good at communicating urgent rural issues. One survey reports that "Save the family farm ... is similar to 'save the whales.' There's a sentimental attachment to a romantic ideal of the family farm, but it's not a very strong one, certainly not strong enough or real enough to have influenced policy."

It's a problem. How do we communicate key issues in sustainable agriculture without having the message devolve into misty, generalized ideas about farming? Or, perhaps worse, have the message go dark around the edges, so that all we hear about is how agriculture is doomed, immune to creative transformation? But, as Vern Grubinger writes here later on, his tongue firmly in his cheek, "In the Midwest they know what sustainable agriculture means. Pronounced 'stainable agriculture,' it's what farming does to your clothes."

Since 1997, Vern Grubinger has been a regular commentator on Vermont Public Radio, and his primary focus has been on explaining to listeners, with accessibility and humor, what is worth knowing about farming and why it matters. He does this, not by preaching, but by materializing on the airwaves during drive time and telling us what he's been doing or thinking as he goes about his work. And he's a busy guy, as the director of the University of Vermont's Center for Sustainable Agriculture and the vegetable and berry specialist for the University of Vermont Cooperative Extension. But what's fun about listening to Vern is that he doesn't talk about being a busy guy; instead, he lets us watch him eat pickled beets, vacuum up swarms of ladybugs, and negotiate with his talkative kids. He plants his garden and takes boxes of worms into the public schools; he visits farms and talks to farmers, even if that means—as it does in this book—going briefly to prison. He answers the phone, shops for peanut butter, and worries about what's really in those chicken nuggets; he describes with obvious joy the slow roasting of a Colorado potato beetle, trapped on black plastic under the hammer of the Vermont sun. In short, Vern talks like us, and he talks to us, and he reclaims agriculture as being interesting, grubby, complicated, and *ours*. His commentaries remind us that the issues that affect agriculture affect everybody, and are part of the fabric of our society.

The Northeast SARE program has compiled this book of radio addresses because we think this is the kind of unsentimental, violin-free talk that's needed, and the kind of talk that reminds us that we are in a food and farming system whether we like it or not. Vern shows us that the choices we make about what to buy, where to buy it, and who gets our money actually matter: Unlike the whales, there is something we can do about farming, and we can do it every night at the dinner table. These choices aren't difficult ones—after all, it's fun going to the farmers' market, with its live music and fragrant produce—but we won't make those choices if we don't believe that our individual actions matter. Vern's radio series, *With an Ear to the Ground*, has always tended to focus on individuals—individual farmers, individual buyers and chefs, and individual voices talking about our food and where it comes from. Vern manages to frame the ideas of sustainable agriculture in ways that matter to us all.

A second impulse behind compiling these radio addresses has to do with the need for the Northeast SARE program to carry the news. The SARE office struggles, not always gracefully, with explaining the scope of sustainable agriculture to our grantees, to our networks of extension, researchers, and nonprofits, and to the general public. We struggle not because we are particularly inept—although some days are better than others—but because the concept of sustainability is interlocking, complicated, and incredibly messy. It's not exclusively about production methods or watersheds or soil health or economic stability, although all those things are important. The difficulty is that the SARE approach to sustainable agriculture also takes into account a great many intangibles. Our outcome statement says that, "Agriculture in the Northeast will be diversified and profitable, providing healthful products to its customers. It will be conducted by farmers who manage resources wisely, who are satisfied with their lifestyles, and have a positive influence on their communities and the environment." This statement is, by definition, open ended. What does it mean to produce healthful food? What does it mean to be satisfied? What constitutes a positive impact on the community? The environment?

This outcome statement—which Vern Grubinger helped the SARE program to develop—is very much a part of the interlocking, complicated, and messy world depicted in this book. Agriculture really does have a role to play in things as different as zoning ordinances, school lunches, and how our children think about the natural world, but conveying that message, keeping it fresh and easy to follow, has not always been easy. By offering up this book, we hope to give the reader a Cook's tour of some of the themes that the Northeast SARE program thinks are part of the sustainability universe, which encompasses everything from national organic production guidelines, predatory wasps, and taking a systems approach to agricultural research, to beaver ponds, September 11, and the nonexistent sex life of potatoes.

Our final reason for raking these essays into a pile was because this modest little book opens a window into a funny and interesting mind, and it's the kind of mind that seems to thrive in the thin soil and demanding climate of the Northeast. Vern speaks for us all when he describes making a run at the home hill during mud season; we know what he's up to when he squints suspiciously at a label. And, since radio tends to be ephemeral—here, then gone—it seems to us that preserving these essays in print is well worth doing if there is a chance it might raise, even incrementally, the general happiness quotient of the world.

— HELEN HUSHER
Northeast Sustainable Agriculture
Research and Education Program

1997

A Vision Thing

Few Vermonters are of the opinion that our farms ought to go. Most of us seem to think they are pretty nice to have around, sprucing up the landscape as they do, helping to attract tourist dollars, and, oh yes, providing food. Our warm fuzzy feelings about local farms are swell, but they're not much help to farmers trying to stay in business.

Farming, as picturesque and romantic as it may seem, is a business, and, when push comes to shove in our society, the business of farming often gets the short end of the stick. The market for many farm products is not truly free, and the playing field is not very level. For example, federally funded water and highway systems are part of a cheap-food policy that masks the true economic and environmental cost of food production. Although Vermont's farms don't use up aquifers, destroy soil, abuse foreign laborers, or need to ship food thousands of miles to population centers, these and other positive attributes are not widely recognized or rewarded.

As a result, Vermont's farms have been steadily disappearing. The 1935 Census of Agriculture reported over 27,000 farms in Vermont, by 1964 there were about 9,000 farms statewide, and by 1992 the number had dropped to about 5,500. Even though the productivity of the remaining farms is high, and even though there are more cows and more milk than ever produced in Vermont, there is still cause for concern. Unless we work to stem the loss of farms in the state, it will just get tougher for the farmers who remain. A critical mass of farms is needed to maintain the existence of available land, farm-equipment suppliers, agricultural advisors, experienced labor, and like-minded neighbors. All these things are necessary if Vermont is to be a place where the next generation of farmers can succeed.

Agriculture is important to the future of Vermont. Not only does it generate half a billion dollars a year in farm-product sales, and several times that in related services and processing, it also lends value to our $2-billion-a-year tourist industry. Although hard to quantify, agriculture also contributes to our sense of place and quality of life. When agriculture occupies the land, it limits development and thus supports the existence of the small towns and the participatory democracy that so many of us cherish.

There's a bright future for Vermont's farms if we work to create strong markets for their products and develop public policies that commit us to protecting agricultural land. There's nothing inherently wrong with industrial and residential development, but they often conflict with agriculture. We need to clarify our vision for Vermont's working landscape, and set policies accordingly. I have a vision of Vermont in which small rural communities continue to thrive, based on an economy that cultivates the interdependent strengths of agriculture, forestry, recreation, tourism, and cottage industry. A different vision of Vermont emphasizes the need for just about any kind of business development, and promotes the kind of building and sprawl and loss of community that goes on just about everywhere else in the nation in the name of jobs, profits, growth, and material well-being. Of course, the choices are not quite this simple, and some aspects of the two visions can coexist. But unless one vision has priority, there will continue to be debate each time a mall is proposed, a landfill needs siting, or a use-value tax abatement program is questioned.

If we aren't going to do what it takes to sustain Vermont's farms, perhaps we should admit it and dispense with giving lip service to agriculture. Then, instead of trying to help farms thrive, we could assist them in converting the land into storage facilities, offices, and agricultural museums, or in selling out to housing developers as the state evolves into something like New Jersey. No offense, but that state exemplifies what could eventually happen to Vermont: a tidal wave of development that swallows up farms and rural communities. I'd rather we act now to avoid that fate.

Decomposition Galore

I may have been a microbe in a previous life, because I get a kick out of composting. Like many gardeners, I compost my kitchen scraps in a molded plastic container, black, that reminds me of Darth Vader, and I have several piles of yard waste compost near the garden. At the office, worm composting takes care of coffee grounds and stale lunches. I also maintain stacks of animal manures from several ruminant species, because I can never decide if I prefer horse, sheep, cow, or goat compost.

There are good reasons for decomposing in so many ways: If you're into farming microbes (and that's what composting is), different types of wastes and different environmental conditions call for different kinds microbe farms, sort of like diversified agriculture. All of these systems, properly managed, produce a similar product: the dark, sweet-smelling soil amendment that gardeners call black gold.

Good compost is the ultimate soil amendment: High in plant nutrients, full of stable organic matter that improves the tilth of soil, and it's cheap if you make it yourself. Making compost is politically correct, too, since it recycles organic wastes instead of sending them to the landfill. And in terms of ecological excitement, well, there's nothing like harnessing the hunger of billions of microorganisms to transform useless carbon by-products into soil fertility.

Thinking like a microbe can be helpful to human composters. Actually, we have a lot in common. We both require a steady supply of oxygen and we both need the right amount of moisture—enough to keep from drying out, but not so much that we drown. And we need a balanced diet—high-carbon stuff like pasta, bread, straw, or leaves mixed with high-nitrogen stuff like legumes, or the urine and feces in manure. Well, our taste in food differs a bit.

The key to making high-quality compost is to have the right combination of wastes to meet the microbes' needs so they will prosper and multiply. Fortunately, composting is easy, since there tends to be just two kinds of materials available to compost: dry, high-carbon stuff that is absorbent and keeps a compost pile fluffy and well aerated, and wet, high-nitrogen stuff that gets stinky pretty quick on its own and is usually a sloppy mess. Mix the two together and you've got a microbial population explosion. Compost scientists call dry high-carbon materials like straw, leaves, shredded paper, and sawdust bulking agents, and these should be stockpiled in anticipation of getting wet high-nitrogen wastes, like grass clippings, food scraps, and fresh manure. The high-nitrogen materials are not pleasant to store in piles around the house, but they don't cause odor problems if promptly and thoroughly mixed with a bulking agent.

Each of my microbe farms has its own feeding strategy. I keep a trash barrel of mowed-up leaves from last fall next to my food scrap composter. A big handful of leaves gets tossed in with each bucket of slop that comes from the kitchen. Near the garden there's a pile where weeds, grass clippings and zucchinis the size of baseball bats get mixed with stacks of old hay, small twigs, dried-up vines, and stalks that are pulled from the garden as crops go by. The piling and layering of these ingredients goes on all season, with an occasional handful of garden fertilizer sprinkled in to assure there's enough nitrogen. The haystack-like pile then sits for a year or two, shrinking in size by at least half, until it's finished enough to put on the blueberries or raspberries. A new haystack gets made each year.

Pickup loads of aged manure from just about every farm critter except emus have graced a spot near my vegetable garden. If the manure has been mixed with enough bedding, turned a few times, and aged like a fine wine, you can just about feel the fertility in a handful of the spongy, peatlike stuff.

I get this nectar of the gods delivered in the fall, cover it, and let it age some more until spring. Then I fork it liberally into my garden rows just prior to seeding or transplanting, relishing how it makes the soil feel, and anticipating how it will make the plants grow.

During the winter, outdoor compost piles become inactive, because my microbial friends are too sluggish to get much done. Thank goodness for the worm box, so I can compost indoors year-round.

A Kindergarten Worm Visit

Every year the kindergarten at Guilford Central School invites me to visit with my traveling worms. These are composting worms, or red wigglers, that transform food and other organic wastes into crumbly black fertilizer. You can find them in old manure piles or you can order them from gardening catalogs. Normally, I keep mine in a large wooden box at the office, where they dispose of a steady flow of coffee grounds, coffee filters, and lunch scraps. When it's time to take the worms on a road trip, I shovel some into a plastic storage tub that's been punched with holes to let air in.

Visiting this kindergarten is like touring a model community. Everything that can be recycled is recycled, using color-coded bins for paper, glass, cardboard, and metal cans. There is a well-worn path to the outdoor compost pile. Every activity area is labeled with a colorful sign. The room is full of displays that show people's connection to the natural world. The idea of using worms to recycle wastes fits right in.

I arrive with my covered box, and the suspense is too much for the kids. They want it opened immediately so they can see the worms—the lecture on vermiculture can wait! I launch into my explanation of the ways and means of worm farming, and the tension builds.

I try to involve the squirming kids in a discussion of worm ecology: "What conditions do worms like?" I ask.

"Dark," offers one child.

"Wet," says another.

"Dirty," says a third.

Okay. "What do worms like to eat?"

A boy raises his hand, digressing about his feelings for worms and the various things he and his brothers have done to worms. The teacher guides the class back on track and repeats the question.

"Worms eat bugs," I'm told.

"Well, not exactly," I respond, wondering whether to clarify the difference between insects and microbes.

"They eat garbage," says another little voice.

"That's right, some kinds of garbage—do they eat glass and metal?" A chorus of *nos* rings out. "They eat things that come from plants," I suggest.

"Like paper?"

"Yes!"

"And wood?"

"If it's shredded up into small pieces they can handle, like sawdust."

"And vegetables, too, don't they?"

"Absolutely."

I explain that worms need some bedding to hang out in, a place they can go that is moist but not sloppy wet, with plenty of air. Shredded-up newspaper, cardboard, or old leaves work well. Then a handful or two of food scraps can be added to the top of the bedding every day. Over time, they will eat up both the bedding and the food, producing worm castings. In a few months, the soil-like castings need to be removed. These can be put in the garden or in potted plants. Then fresh bedding has to be added to keep the worms happy.

"What happens to the worms when you take out the castings?" they want to know.

"There is a way to keep most of them in the box," I assure them. "Because worms don't like bright light, you can take the lid off the box and they will move deep down into the castings, away from the light. Then you can skim off the top few inches of castings without removing the worms."

Now the children are into it, and it's time to unveil the stars of the show. The small bodies crowd closely around me and peer into the dark box as I lift the lid. In the next few seconds, a hundred skinny red worms slither out of sight, diving away from the surface of the compost as soon as they sense the light. The kids excitedly share their thoughts: "Look, they're afraid." "Those worms aren't very big." "Can I touch one?"

I select a specimen and it's passed from little hand to little hand, poked and rolled about to ensure that it's really alive.

"Is it a boy or a girl?" Someone had to ask.

"Well…, actually it's both." I glance at the teacher. Her eyes implore me—*don't even go there*—but it's too late, I can't wiggle out of this one. "Worms are hermaphrodites, which means each one is a boy *and* a girl."

Now I'm looked at with suspicion; this worm guy is obviously not to be trusted. I carry on bravely. "Two worms get together, like a mom and a dad, and then they *both* produce an egg. You want to see some worm eggs?" *There*, I think, *I'm off the hook.*

Fast as I can, I pick out a few lemon-shaped eggs the size of small peppercorns. These get passed around as I explain the less confusing aspects of worm reproduction. "Several worms can hatch from each egg, which are really called cocoons. The baby worms look like little white threads when they're born." The littlest worms are too delicate to pass around, so I make my way around the circle so everybody gets a good look at the newborns. I think my credibility is restored. Class is over, and I am given a recital of *thank-yous* and presented with a ribbon. It says To Dr. Worm from the Guilford Kindergarten, and it's decorated with squiggly worms. Back at my office, I feel truly honored as I hang this recognition on my wall.

Apples: Going Organic

Miller Orchards, in my home town of Dummerston, Vermont, is the largest producer of organic apples on the East Coast. Read Miller, a member of the seventh generation to run the farm, is a man who doesn't mince words. "Organic orcharding isn't feasible," he told me on my first farm visit, shortly after I was hired by the University of Vermont, "and I'm getting pretty tired of training new extension agents every couple of years, so I hope you'll stick around."

At that time, Read practiced IPM, or integrated pest management. Using all the newest techniques, he had dramatically reduced conventional pesticide use on the farm while maintaining high yields. The problem was that the market did not reward him for his good stewardship efforts. In fact, apple prices went from bad to worse: In 1992 it was barely worth packing out a bushel of apples that sold for four dollars. But, at the same time, organic apples were going for ten times that.

The following winter, Read called my office asking for a copy of Vermont's organic farming standards, put together by the Northeast Organic Farming Association, or NOFA. He was wondering if dormant oil, used to smother scale and mites in the early spring, was permitted under organic standards, and I said it was. He asked whether sulfur could be used to manage apple scab, and I replied yes. I could see the wheels turning in his head—perhaps it *was* possible to grow apples organically.

Since apples have many serious pests, using no pesticides at all isn't an option if you want unblemished fruit, which is the only kind that consumers will buy. If Read had asked, I would have advised him against organic orcharding, because I believed the dogma that apples were just not suited to organic production because organic pesticides were ineffective, harsh on beneficial insects, and expensive. A Cornell study said so, so it must be true.

But Read didn't ask; instead, he simply set his mind to figuring out how to do it. It is now five years later, and he manages 180 acres of certified organic apples, with more acreage coming on line soon. I visited his farm and saw blocks of trees loaded with large, unblemished fruit. He made sure to also show me blocks of trees with small, pest-damaged fruit, too. "We've got to do a better job managing these blocks," he said. "This year, about half the farm's crop will have to go to cider, but the price premium for organic apples more than makes up for that."

Read went on. "Every year I learn more about how to do this," he said. "I've made a lot of mistakes, and it's cost me a bundle of money to get this far, but it's like a marriage: You have to be in it for the long haul, and there's no cheating allowed." Read has learned that the timing of organic insect- and disease-control sprays is even more critical than with conventional sprays, and he is working on ways to spray his thousands of trees faster. He is refining organic methods of using fish emulsion to fertilize trees and steam heat to control weeds. The drawbacks to organic apple production are real—more spraying, higher costs, and more blemishes—but, at least on this farm, swearing off synthetic pesticides and fertilizers has opened up markets that may be the key to its economic sustainability.

Other orchardists in the state have been growing organic apples a lot longer, notably Nick Cowles of Shelburne Orchards, who has been experimenting with organic and ecological production techniques for two decades. The knowledge that he and others like him have developed and shared is what laid the groundwork for success at Miller Orchard. But the moral of this story is not about organic orcharding, and it's not even about apples. It's about why people change the way they farm.

First, there's got to be some incentive—in this case an economic one. Second, the farmer needs a keen understanding of the ecosystem he or she is working with—in this case a lifetime of observation and experience in the orchard. And third, something has to open the farmer's mind to new possibilities. In this case it was a trip to China.

A couple of summers ago, Read went to China as a consultant; he had been hired to teach First-World fruit growing technology to a developing nation. He saw lots of fruit trees, lots of fruit, and virtually no advanced technology. The experience made him reconsider our way of doing things, and it expanded his vision of orchard-management possibilities.

In farming and most other professions, including Cooperative Extension, people go through stages of knowledge. You start out knowing that you don't know squat. Then, after a number of years, you come to believe that you know quite a lot. Then later, you realize again just how much you don't know. Some of the best farmers I know act like they are just discovering how the whole thing works, because they learn so much each and every year they farm. Humility and a thirst for knowledge are a healthy combination when your livelihood depends on collaboration with Mother Nature.

The Working Landscape from Above

J et travel is not your usual method of agricultural education, but it can teach the observant traveler a lot about farming, mostly by showing us that agriculture is alive, widespread, and beautiful to the eye. Flying makes me think about agriculture, and I always ask for a window seat so I can look down on the land and contemplate how it's being used. Agriculture's dominance of the landscape across our country is impressive: The census folks tell us we're down to just under a million farms, the fewest since the Civil War, but from the air they seem to be everywhere, sometimes stretching as far as the eye can see, interrupted occasionally by a small town at a crossroads.

The cities are an exception of course, and when we are at 35,000 feet and moving at 500 miles an hour, their approach is forewarned by blemishes in the pastoral landscape: The farm communities are no longer contiguous and fields become interspersed with warehouses, subdivisions, and highways. The buildings rise up toward the airplane and all signs of plant life disappear, except for rectangles of green here and there that are the parks and playgrounds. Then, just as quickly, urban structures fade away and fields reappear, first alone, then in clusters, and soon the landscape is again covered by swaths and squares of green, brown, and gold.

From my cramped seat in coach class, there are signs of discomfort in the agriculture far below. Besides the obvious loss of farmland to development, water resources appear threatened in parts of the country. In dry lands out West, the fields are not square but round, where water for growing crops has been spewed in great circles by center-pivot irrigation, depleting underground aquifers. In New England, we're blessed with an abundance of rainfall that produces a naturally green landscape, much of it in forest. Even southern New England is largely green hills and fields, with suburbs and cities fewer and farther between than the Friday-night interstate traffic into Vermont would suggest. And there are farm fields, too, of diversified operations such as nurseries, tobacco, vegetables, and dairy. Jetting north into Vermont the fields get more numerous, especially in the valleys. In the hills, farms appear to radiate outward from a village until they run up against mountains and forest. While trees dominate much of our green and mountainous state, there are large areas of farmland in the Champlain Valley and north-central Vermont where the terrain is flatter and the soils are fertile. It is here that Vermont's dairy industry is concentrated, and where the majority of New England's milk is produced. From the sky, the importance of dairy farming to the beauty of our working landscape is impossible to ignore.

From the air, it is also clear that farming does not follow artificial human boundaries. Instead, it has adapted to the natural landscape, seeking out the better soils and climates and sizing its fields to fit geological constraints. Yet even here agriculture appears vulnerable, apparently unable to resist the onslaught of suburbia that gushes from the cities.

The view from above reinforces my conviction that Vermont is a special place. It contains a manageable number of people, and it has been spared the huge scars of urban infrastructure on its land. The hills are blessed with vast expanses of forest rather than isolated stands; the lowlands are blessed with enough topsoil, water, and open space to support crop and animal production. The abundance of small towns, with just one or two thousand people, and the many working farms that average just a few hundred acres seem so appropriate to what the land has to offer. I'm not against development or large-scale farming per se, but if you need reminding that Vermont's special landscape deserves thoughtful planning and meaningful protection, I suggest you fly the friendly skies over most any other state.

1998

Mud Season

Normally I'm quite fond of soil. I love the spongy feel of a silt loam underfoot when I visit a river-bottom vegetable farm, I relish the smell of freshly turned earth in my garden, and I can sense magic in that mix of minerals, microbes, air, and water that we so often take for granted. But for a few weeks each year, this soil is just dirt to me.

Those few weeks are called mud season, a time when the soil under the fifty-four miles of unpaved road in my town turns to mush. To the black-top dwellers, mud season is an amusing concept; to my neighbors and me, it's serious business.

As our hillside wakes from winter's permafrost, the snow melts and the top few inches of ground thaws. The water can't percolate down through the frozen subsoil, so it blends with the solid part of our dirt road to form a colloidal suspension. That's what physicists call Jell-O. The resulting quagmire eats small cars and makes the task of getting to and from town more exciting than a riding a roller coaster.

You need the right vehicle to travel the mud. Two-wheel-drive cars get parked at the bottom of the hill when the mud demons are angriest. Four-wheel-drive machinery has a high survival rate, but only if properly equipped. And forget about those all-season tires labeled for mud and snow, since they aren't very good in either; those who master the mud ride on tires sporting raised white letters saying things like DESERT COMMAND or SPEED KING, which is odd, since the mud has nothing to do with either deserts or speed.

Technique is important, too. Even the best-prepared will fail if their attention to the mud wanders, perhaps while they're listening to the radio or enjoying the view of the woods as they drive. No, they must feel the mud as they go, stepping hard on the gas and heaving the steering wheel to and fro when it attempts to swallow them up.

My heart pounds when I leave the pavement and enter the mud zone. I look up the hill scarred with ruts and see that some of them are two feet deep, slick and shiny, and ready to gobble up tires. I rev the engine, put it into gear, and charge upward. Rocking from side to side, my tires spin as I slowly advance toward the safety of home; the soil splatters in the wheel wells loud and hard. Suddenly there's a decrease in speed and it's the moment of truth. I grip the wheel tightly and put the pedal to the metal. Stopping now would be surrender. Inch by inch, I lurch forward until the treads grasp some solid matter, and I'm moving freely again. I exhale and smile: I made it.

Next day, the temperatures have plummeted. The road is a like a frozen railroad track, but one that is all over the place, like after an earthquake. Gullies and hills as solid as icebergs await, ready to rip the undersides from cars that show too little respect. I drive a careful path, bumping and bouncing down the hill, straining to look ahead, fearing a really deep rut that will take me wherever it likes.

Speed is the *enemy* now. Go too fast and you'll be slammed around like a pinball; go too slow and you won't get to work until noon. If there's delicate cargo on board and you're in a rush, it's a bummer. I'll never forget the time I had my very pregnant wife in the pickup and we were late for an appointment. The ruts were frozen and unforgiving. I hate being late, but I also didn't want to deliver the baby on the way. Even at twenty miles an hour her belly heaved mightily about, almost independent of the rest of her. She smiled; I clenched my jaw. At long last we reached the bottom of the hill, still a family of two.

It makes me smile when city friends visit and ask, as they always do, "How's the road in winter?" They are worried about the snow, of course.

"Oh, the town has it plowed and sanded by seven in the morning after every storm," I reply. "It's the mud that we worry about."

They look at me quizzically.

"Come back and visit next spring," I tell them. "You'll see."

Intensive Pasture Management
Is Grass Farming

I know just enough about animals to be dangerous. The truth is, I'm a plant person. Plants are easy to deal with; they can't run away, don't make much noise, and never get named, so I don't feel bad when I eat them. The only livestock I've ever raised had little or nothing to do with farming: I have gone in mostly for cats, toddlers, and worms. So it was a bit daunting when I became director of the University of Vermont Center for Sustainable Agriculture. After all, animal agriculture accounts for more than three-quarters of the farm economy in Vermont.

Sometimes ignorance is bliss. A lack of preconceived notions can free the mind up to ask simple questions. As I learned more about dairy farming, one question my mind asked was *Why don't cows eat more grass?*

Sure, you see cows out to pasture, snacking on grass in between their main meals at the barn, where corn, hay, and other materials are mixed by farmers to provide the balanced diet necessary for high milk production. The typical dairy farm in Vermont practices what's called confinement feeding, where cows spend a lot of time in the barn, so most of their feed must be brought to them, and most of their manure must be moved out. A very different method of dairying is called intensive pasture management, or rotational grazing.

Pioneered in New Zealand, rotational grazing hardly resembles what I see happening on the many dairy farms I drive by. Day after day, cows are let out to the same large pasture to get some exercise and eat a bit of grass until it's time to go back to the barn for dinner. But rotational grazing means moving the cows from one section of pasture to another, in some cases up to several times a day. Once the herd munches all the plants down to a few inches from the ground, they are moved into a new area, full of lush growth that in turn will quickly be chewed down. Pastures are sectioned off using portable electric fencing, and water is supplied to every section of pasture. The quality and quantity of the pasture growth must be managed to get the best feed for the cows, and this is done by adjusting the size of the pastures, the number of cows in them, and the length of time they stay in a given pasture.

Rotational grazing has been researched and promoted here in Vermont by Professor Bill Murphy of the University of Vermont Plant and Soil Science Department. Dr. Murphy realized that the more cows collected their own feed and spread their own manure, the less it would cost the farmer to make milk. Besides the potential financial benefits, rotational grazing is also attractive from an ecological point of view: Good pasture management can produce high-quality feed without tilling the soil. Farmers must still put up hay for the winter, and some grain is needed to give the cows a balanced diet, but the benefits are substantial. On some Vermont farms it's cheaper to purchase corn than it is to grow it.

So why doesn't everyone switch to rotational grazing? One reason is that cows on pasture tend to produce less milk than their confinement-fed cousins on a richer diet, especially during the transition to high-quality pastures, a process that can take several years. That means reduced gross income, even though net income may improve because of savings on production costs. Another reason for not switching is that some farmers have productive fields that grow high yields of corn; they've got a lot of investment in their current system, and it works for them. These farmers often feel that rotational grazing just isn't appropriate to their farm. But some farmers, like David and Mary Ellen Franklin of Guilford, say rotational grazing has saved their farm. They've got hilly terrain, less-than-prime agricultural soils, and their corn-growing equipment was old and expensive to maintain.

Changing the way you farm requires new investments and new skills. However, many farmers are eager to consider alternatives and, as a result, interest in grazing is growing. As one farmer put it, "The closer my back gets to the wall, the bigger my ears get." The Center for Sustainable Agriculture is trying to help farmers learn more about rotational grazing, most often by working with the Vermont Grass Farmers Association, the Natural Resource Conservation Service, UVM Extension, and the Department of Agriculture to organize workshops, on-farm pasture walks, and farmer discussion groups that support grazers with information. We are not trying to convert every farm to rotational grazing, nor are we implying that confinement feeding is a bad thing. Our goal is simply to provide farmers with as many options as possible as they strive to sustain their farms into the future.

The Draft Rule for Organic Standards

The federal government is proposing to pull a fast one on organic farmers, although it has to be noted that it's taken them eight years to do it. The USDA—the United States Department of Agriculture—recently released their plan to regulate organic farming, and the plan, and the feelings about it, are so bad that organic farmers across the country are in a collective snit, burning up the Internet with scathing e-mail.

It all started with a thoughtful and well-written piece of legislation, sponsored by Vermont Senator Pat Leahy, called the Organic Foods Production Act of 1990. This law was designed to promote organic farming and to protect consumers and farmers by creating national standards for organic food. Farmers and processors in every state would have to adhere to the same guidelines in order to legally use the word *organic* to describe their products.

The devil, of course, is in the details. Since the original law did not describe all the materials and practices that could or couldn't be used on organic farms, or exactly how organic farms would get certified, that part was left up to the USDA to determine, based on advice from a National Organic Standards Board. After five years of taking public testimony, the standards board developed recommendations that were passed on to the USDA for the creation of a draft rule that included all the specifics. The rule was then passed around to other federal agencies for their input.

Reportedly, it was the changes made by the Environmental Protection Agency, the Food and Drug Administration, and the Office of Management and Budget that really caused problems. What resulted is a proposed set of standards that fails to prohibit the use of irradiation, sewage sludge, genetically engineered organisms, or factory-style farms in the production of certified organic food. The proposal also weakens existing requirements for raising organic livestock, and it opens the door for the addition of synthetic ingredients to organic foods during processing. By diluting the requirements for organic certification, the proposal violates the intent of the original law and threatens the credibility of organic food in the marketplace.

These weak standards would not be the minimum required for certification, but would be the *strictest* standards that state or private certification programs could require. Setting higher standards, or creating a different label to describe a more rigorous definition of organic farming, could be illegal. Even terms such as *grown without synthetic chemicals*, or *raised without antibiotics* might be prohibited under the proposal. Talk about limiting consumer choice!

Vermont's organic farmers and consumers are fortunate in that we have NOFA, the Northeast Organic Farming Association, which has done a great job running and growing the Vermont Organic Farmers certification program. Thanks to the work of their dedicated staff, thoughtful farmers, and support from state agencies, there are now 170 organic farms and processors certified in Vermont. It already costs between $150 and $550 a year to get certified in Vermont, a fee that is assessed on gross organic sales. Yet the proposed USDA rule could raise certification fees significantly, as a way to fund federal oversight of the program. This would make organic certification impractical for many small farmers. If you think about it, it's ironic that farmers should have to pay the government for the right to tell consumers that they have gone the extra mile to produce healthy food.

Thank goodness we live in a democracy, and there's still hope that this flawed rule can be fixed. After a public comment period, the USDA will review the input they get before issuing a final rule. That rule is likely to make or break the future of organic farming in Vermont.

The Russians Come to Town

Imagine that California, Florida, and Texas have seceded from the nation. So have North and South Dakota, and they're at war. A loaf of bread costs twenty bucks. General Motors, Archer Daniels Midland, and Pepsico have split up into dozens of small companies, run by former clerks, salesmen, and accountants, many of whom must pay protection money to local gangs if they want to stay in business. Most of the large corporate farms in the heartland are bankrupt, their remains divided up and distributed to hundreds of would-be farmers, some with experience, some without. Thousands of tractors lie idle because spare parts cannot be found, hardly any fertilizer is available, and much of the land has been eroded or contaminated by previous mismanagement.

There—can you imagine it? Then you're imagining what it's like to be in Russia. At least that's the picture I got after spending a few days with a team of Russians that came to Vermont for training in sustainable agriculture and extension work. Their visit was sponsored by the Center for Citizen's Initiative, a San Francisco nonprofit that specializes in exchanges with the former Soviet Union.

The group's leader, Valentin Alexandrovich Smirnov, a high-ranking official in the Ministry of Agriculture, appeared to be right out of a storybook. Barrel-chested, with a shock of silver hair under his Russian fur cap, a beet-red face, and a mouthful of gold teeth, he was prone to making elaborate toasts and correcting the explanations of his lower-ranking colleagues. The others—professors of horticulture, soil science, and farm management—will be running the brand-new extension centers established throughout Russia. These directors are not ivory-tower academics; in fact, many of them also run small subsistence farms in an effort to put food on the table and supplement their income.

These Russians spent three days in the classroom, learning about Vermont's efforts to improve manure management, encourage soil stewardship, promote rotational grazing, and use computers to keep records of crop production. On alternate days they hit the road, visiting farmers and agricultural organizations. They got their first-ever taste of maple syrup at Dave Marvin's Butternut Mountain Farm in Johnson, and nodded approvingly. They went to Jack and Anne Lazor's farm in Westfield and checked it out inch by inch, from the Jersey cows in the barn to the bulk tank, the grain grinder, the yogurt plant, even the equipment shed.

They were treated to a homegrown lunch before they got a mud-season tour of Lani Fondiller's farmstead. She explained her diversified, self-sufficient farmstead that raises sheep and goats and produces wool for felting and milk for making cheese. We toured her one-room production kitchen, then walked down the hill to the custom-made cave where the cheeses are aged.

The Russians also visited the farms of Burlington's Intervale, David Miskell's organic tomato greenhouse, Shelburne Farms, and the UVM dairy farm. They really enjoyed meeting hardworking rural Americans at least as much as they appreciated learning about farming in Vermont. They were struck by the independence and self-determination of our farmers and small business people. "Your farmers do what they want, and they have shown me what it means to be a person," one of them told me. I was reminded of a slogan from America's inner cities: "I am somebody!"

Despite the enormous challenges that these Russians face, they have hope for the future because opportunity and liberty are on the increase. That, coupled with their commitment to stewardship, should go a long way toward turning things around. For my part, feeling the Russians' optimism and thirst for knowledge reminded me of what extension is all about: improving the quality of people's lives by providing practical information. Despite all our own problems, the grass sure seems green on this side of the fence right now.

Internships on Farms

My grandfather was an urban blue-collar worker who came here from eastern Europe. To him, working with your hands was the burden of the lower classes. "Whaddaya wanna be a farmer for?" I can remember him asking me. At the time I was attending an agricultural university, and I probably did want to be a farmer. But I was learning precious little about farming. Instead, I was getting trained in the theory rather than the practice of agriculture.

I was starving for practical experience. Having grown up in suburbia, I arrived at school without any farming skills. After several years in the classroom, I realized that if I was going to get familiar with the realities of agriculture, there wasn't much choice—I'd have to leave school. I went off and became a partner in a small vegetable and fruit farm. This taught me a lot—for example, I learned that the only way we could pay the mortgage was by landscaping rather than growing food, that farming is really hard work, and that partnerships don't last forever. So after a few years I returned to school.

This time I sought out practical training. My first semester back, I took a noncredit course called Practical Farm Techniques. It was taught by an old-timer who had formerly worked on the research farm. Every Tuesday afternoon he took his class full of kids like me—suburbanites turned agricultural scientists—out to local farms to milk cows, shear sheep, make hay, and change the oil in ancient Farmall tractors. It was a humbling experience. I learned how hard it is to plow a straight furrow, how much strength it takes to stack hay bales on a wagon all afternoon, and how much skill it takes to back a big wagon into a narrow barn. I spent the better part of an afternoon trying to do that, without success. The farm-hands watching from nearby got a good chuckle out of that.

Eventually I graduated and joined the extension service. Now I had serious reason to rue my limited practical experience. I was supposed to be giving advice to farmers! Well, the farmers helped me get up to speed with liberal doses of reality checks, and after a while I found ways to get hold of information that seemed to be of use to them. In working with young farmers, it became apparent to me that my frustration at having earned an agricultural degree without getting much hands-on experience is widely shared.

Last year, the Center for Sustainable Agriculture at the University of Vermont decided to develop an agricultural internship program that would assure meaningful on-the-job learning and allow students to earn academic credit for their on-farm experience. After all, every student graduating with an agriculture degree from a land-grant university should have the oppor-tunity to get familiar with a real farm and a real farmer. This program is unique because, besides offering credit, it also pays the student a stipend for time spent on a farm-based academic inquiry, supplementing what the farmer pays for the time the student spends on regular farm chores.

The sustainable agriculture internship program requires a learning con-tract between the farmer and the student where both commit to working together on a specific project, and they also agree ahead of time about how the intern's time will be divided between the academic project and the farm labor. Before interns are placed, a thorough application must be filled out by potential interns and willing hosts, which include agricultural or-ganizations as well as farmers. The students contact the hosts, and the two parties interview each other and work out housing and scheduling issues before signing a contract.

In the first year of the program, eleven students were placed in intern-ships. Their projects included such topics as biological pest control in or-chards, rotational grazing methods, cover cropping to control greenhouse pests, converting from conventional to organic dairying, and the nutrition of dairy goats, to name a few.

Now the 1998 internship program is underway, with the goal of placing twice as many interns as last year. Our goal is not just to increase students' understanding of agriculture. We also want to provide the opportunity to develop lifelong learning skills in a challenging, real-world situation that requires students put academic knowledge to work, engage in teamwork, communicate and solve problems effectively, and think clearly and critically. After all, these are the skills that lead to success, whether in farming or any other enterprise.

The Vermont Fresh Network

There may be some debate as to whether Vermont is a Great *Lake* State,* but there should be no doubt that we live in a Great *Food* State. Where else would hundreds of chefs and farmers team up to that link people who *produce* food for a living and people who *prepare* food for a living? It's called the Vermont Fresh Network.

Restaurants in the network buy directly from local farms and food processors, instead of going through a distributor. This means there are no middlemen to pay, and the food takes a direct route to the buyer with a minimum of travel. This arrangement fosters communication between chefs and farmers, and helps to build reliable markets that pay a fair price for high-quality goods from our farms. As a result, the Vermont Fresh Network is contributing to the sustainability of Vermont's agriculture. Of course, the whole thing would just be a bunch of hot air if it weren't for the fact that Vermont farms are the source of a vast array of very delicious food.

Have you tried Vermont Shepherd cheese? Or Butterworks Farm maple yogurt? How about Killdeer Farm tomatoes, The Organic Cow chocolate milk, or a Stonewood Farm turkey? In season, there's a bounty of fresh berries, vegetables, apples, and maple syrup that comes from our very own hills

---

* In 1998, President Clinton signed a bill declaring Lake Champlain one of the Great Lakes so that Vermont and New York could get federal money to research the environmental health of the Champlain Basin. Loud howls of protest rose from the Midwest. One commentator explained, not all that politely, that Champlain was "a pretty good lake, but not great." The designation was dropped, but Vermont still got the money. —Ed.

and valleys. Why would a chef—or a consumer for that matter—want mileage-weary food from a thousand miles away when they've got access to hundreds of high-quality products made by families running farms and businesses just down the road a piece? It's true: In Vermont, you *can* eat the landscape, and when you do, you contribute to the vitality of the countryside.

Personal relationships between food producers and consumers make our food system a lot healthier, and a lot more fun. When you get to know the farmers at a farmers' market, chatting them up every Saturday of the summer, you feel really good about eating their products. By visiting a farm and watching cider being pressed, cows being milked, or crops being harvested you'll get connected to the food from that farm. Become a Community Supported Agriculture member, and you'll have a farm that feels like an old friend. Restaurants can help people connect to farms, too.

At the Putney Inn, farms that supply the food are listed right on the menu. From July to October, 90 percent of the food the inn buys comes from thirty local producers, all within a hundred-mile radius. Ann Cooper, the executive chef, told me, "When I joined the Vermont Fresh Network several years ago, I knew that Vermont had great food products, but I thought that many of them were expensive. It took me a while to understand that the true cost of local food really *isn't* higher because there's less waste, better quality, and more consistent guest satisfaction. Now I realize that chefs have a responsibility to work toward a sustainable food system. If we don't support local farmers, pretty soon the beautiful scenery will disappear, then the tourists will stop coming, and we'll be out of business. So it really makes sense to buy locally and seasonally."

Bill Nixon of Green Pastures Farm in Braintree sells all seventy of the lambs he produces each year directly to his six restaurant partners. "The chefs I work with recognize the high quality of Vermont pasture-raised lamb," he told me. "It's got a unique, full-flavored taste, and it's a lot leaner than lamb from out West."

Through the Vermont Fresh Network, culinary folk and stewards of the land continue to educate each other. They meet on the farms as well as in the kitchens, and they also get together for an annual forum that features the latest and greatest foods of the state. The forum offers workshops on how to sell to restaurants or maybe introduce cheeses on the menu. And the lunches at these gatherings, as you can imagine, are truly awesome.

The Ecological Revolution

M y faith in the future has been renewed, and this happened at a forum where some smart people and some big businesses described how we're going to get from the Industrial to the Ecological Revolution. The message was that doing good by the planet is ecologically possible *and* economically profitable.

The event was sponsored by POETS, the Partnership of Environmental Technology and Science, a group of forward-thinking Vermont business and agency leaders who support policies and technologies that are compatible with the environment. Over 600 people were in the audience, yet we filled only a fraction of the cavernous breeding barn at Shelburne Farms where the panelists assembled. The ideas that flowed were large, too, because they addressed the question *What will our future be?*

One option is to continue on our current path, treating Earth and its resources only as commodities, building a global economy in which megacorporations dominate, inequity is widespread, and we threaten future generations with our consumption and waste. Or we can take ecological design principles and apply them to agriculture, transportation, energy, manufacturing, and more. That approach could reconcile nature and business, build a culture of respect and caring, and protect the well-being of generations yet unborn.

To take the high road, we have to transform the way our culture thinks about the world, because these problems can't be solved by the same processes that created them. Instead of trying to fine-tune the systems that pollute and consume, we need entirely new systems that cleanse and re-cycle. Rather than trying to reduce waste, our goal should be to eliminate it. I was surprised to learn that a lot of technology already exists to do this. It's our policies and behaviors that have to change; the challenge is more spiritual and ethical than it is scientific. The question is, *Do we care enough about the future to change the present?* Because once there's an ecological revolution in our minds and hearts, then it will follow in our commerce.

At the forum we heard from the CEO of a billion-dollar corporation that makes carpet tiles, and also has a goal of doing no harm to the Earth. After eliminating toxic materials from their production process and developing a marketing plan in which they take back and reuse old carpet instead of landfilling it, this company saved $50 million in three years.

Designers described how buildings can generate more energy than they consume, can be powered by sunshine, and can give off zero discharge. *No* smokestacks, not smaller smokestacks. These structures already exist, and more are under construction for corporate headquarters and universities that want a truly green campus.

The experts told us that Vermont imports three-quarters of all the energy it uses, more than a billion dollars' worth each year. They pointed out that we can keep this money in the state and create jobs if we become energy independent. Solar technologies are getting more efficient and less expensive all the time, and the industry is growing by over 30 percent a year. Wind power already provides electricity for 2,000 homes in Vermont, and our state is a leader in the manufacturing of wind technology. There are fuel cells, ground-source heat pumps, and other cool gizmos that can help us meet our energy needs and expand the economy if we develop the policies and education to promote their adoption.

We heard about farmers opting for ecological effectiveness instead of short-term efficiency, staying small and practicing stewardship for reasons of health, not regulations. Their products, such as grass-fed livestock, hand-crafted cheeses, and organic vegetables, often find a niche in the competitive marketplace. The profitability of many more farms in Vermont would improve if there was true cost accounting for the natural resource depletion caused by our country's cheap food policies.

The choice is not *growth* or *no growth* so much as it is *what kind of growth*. If Vermont declares its intention to build a sustainable future, makes the necessary investments, and creates the appropriate incentives, then its citizens, our children's children, and the environment will all benefit. And yes, business and the economy will, too.

Beef Production in Vermont

I was passing through Texas a few years ago on an endless interstate, listening to country music because that's what I thought I ought to listen to in Texas, and besides, that's all there was on the radio. In between cowboy croonings a deejay came on, gave the news and weather, and then said, "This is KTXS. Eat More Beef."

Well, the beef industry in Vermont is still a ways from being a tagline on the radio or at the core of popular culture, but it is growing. Over the past five years, membership in the Vermont Beef Producers Association has doubled to encompass more than 200 farms, and there are another couple of hundred producers who have yet to join. Thanks to new marketing opportunities, it's not as hard to make a profit raising beef cattle as it was a few years ago. That's important, because animal-based agriculture is essential to keeping the land open and maintaining our working landscape. Beef farming, whether a full-time or a part-time endeavor, is an option for land use that can help keep hayfields and pastures abundant in the hills of Vermont.

As with all types of farming, a viable market is the key to success. The vast majority of Vermont's beef farmers sells live animals, not meat. Selling meat requires dealing with the costs and regulations associated with slaughtering, packaging, and distribution. So, until recently, Vermont farmers simply shipped their cattle to general livestock auctions and got what they could for them, which wasn't much. Many of the beef buyers at these auctions purchase animals to be made into pet food, and the prices they pay are pretty depressing if you're selling high-quality animals. Then several years ago, the Vermont Department of Agriculture and the Beef Producers Association teamed up to organize spring and fall sales of high-quality beef cattle. At a recent sale, nearly 700 animals were sold at nationally competitive prices.

According to Caleb Scott, a beef farmer from Tinmouth, "Our animals are as good as those produced anywhere in the country, and we've got a very healthy product. We raise grass-fed cattle on pasture when it's warm and they eat mostly homegrown forage crops in the winter. Now that we've pooled our animals together, the word is getting out that there's a significant supply of high-quality Vermont beef. Buyers come from all over the place to purchase our animals. One guy even comes from Nebraska and fills up a semi tractor trailer."

The spring stocker sale is a good place for small farms to purchase beef cattle to put on their pastures, where the animals can gain weight at minimal expense. At the fall feeder sale, these animals may be sold to larger farms that have a good supply of stored feed and can afford to fatten them up (a process known as finishing) for sale to a processor. Currently, only a few beef farmers in Vermont finish their own animals and then sell the meat directly to consumers.

Caleb is one of them, and he told me: "For twenty years I've been selling meat under my own label and sales have steadily increased. Now I raise 100 animals a year on 150 acres of pasture and 100 acres of hay land. There's a very strong niche market out there for locally produced healthy meat. Not only have I got a lot of local customers, but other people drive fifty or sixty miles to the farm to buy my beef. Some of these people are chemically sensitive, and they appreciate a product raised without chemicals. I also supply a half-dozen stores, and there's even more demand, but I don't want to spend too much time driving and making deliveries. I'm fortunate there's a slaughterhouse in Rutland that's just twenty miles away, but if that were to shut down, I'd be out of the retail meat business. The way it is now, by avoiding the middleman I can sell meat at prices comparable to the supermarket and still make a profit."

The lack of slaughterhouses is an obstacle to increasing the supply of Vermont-grown meat, but it's a chicken-or-egg problem. If there were more farms producing animals for meat, then it would be more profitable for slaughterhouses to operate, and there would be more of them. Yet until there are more local slaughterhouses, most farmers can't afford to transport their animals to get processed, so they don't sell meat. A solution to this problem down the road may be a wholesale cooperative with a centrally located processing facility. That could provide a steady market for producers and assure a steady supply of beef for Vermont restaurants and grocery stores.

Biological Control, or Aliens
Ate My Aphids!

I f you're an aphid with a taste for tomato plants, the words *biological control*, often shortened to *biocontrol*, make you quiver with fear right down to your honeytubes. You'd rather not think about predators and parasites with a voracious appetite for you and yours, especially since their eating habits would qualify them for a starring role in an *Aliens* movie. An encounter with these carnivorous insects will leave you longing for a quick and merciful death by pesticides.

For example, there's *Aphidius*, a tiny wasp that injects its egg into the abdomen of a young aphid nymph. The egg hatches and the growing wasp slowly consumes the aphid's innards. When all the food is gone, the wasp cuts a neat exit hole in the backside of the host and emerges, leaving behind a hollow aphid shell.

Young aphids that want to avoid this kind of unpleasantness and become adults had also better be on the lookout for *Aphidoletes*. These mosquito-like flies seek out congregations of aphids and lay hundreds of eggs in their vicinity. The eggs soon hatch into fast-moving larvae with a hankering for aphid meat. They run after the aphids, bite them on the knees, and inject them with a paralyzing toxin. Then they literally suck their guts out. On a good day a single *Aphidoletes* larva can chow down on fifty aphids.

Several species of ladybugs also have aphids on the menu. Less horrific than some of their biocontrol buddies, ladybugs simply chase aphids down and gobble them up. The convergent lady beetle is collected from the foothills of the mountains in California, where it congregates in masses, and is then sold to farmers and gardeners. It can be kept in refrigerated storage for weeks, even months, and released when needed to keep aphids in check. That's handy for the growers who buy them, because these ladybugs like to eat and run: They tend to fly away after a short while, probably trying to find their way back to the West Coast.

Right now, there are several dozen commercially available biocontrol organisms. Most are reared in specialized labs and sold to farmers growing greenhouse crops; in the enclosed space of a greenhouse, the insect pests and their enemies can't avoid bumping into each other. The pests won't leave the greenhouse and abandon their food source, and the predators and parasites hang around and multiply as long as there are pests to eat and the environmental conditions are suitable. So the race is on: Pests eat the crop and reproduce as fast as they can, pursued by predators and parasites that consume the pests and reproduce as fast as they can. If all goes well for the farmer, the biocontrols eat and mate faster than the pests, which are kept in check, but are not necessarily eliminated.

Biological control is an exciting alternative to pesticides for controlling greenhouse pests. Organic growers like David Chapman of Long Wind Farm in East Thetford are committed to using this technique to protect their crops. With an acre and a half of greenhouses, David is one of the largest organic producers of greenhouse tomatoes in the country, and he's got a lot riding on biocontrols. "We always have some pests," he says, "and we are constantly releasing predators and parasites. Usually the good guys win, but we've learned a few lessons the hard way. Each year we understand more about which biocontrol organisms will be best for managing the pests we have, and what conditions will promote their success."

Biocontrols can be expensive, and they don't work instantly, but they're growing in popularity as farmers learn how to use them effectively. This is one case where biological warfare is a good thing, although the aphids may beg to differ.

Downsizing the Garden

Some people hate gardening. Perhaps they had to do too much weeding as a kid, or maybe they've watched too much Martha Stewart as an adult. It's frustrating to pretend you can have a perfect-looking garden without getting dirty or perspiring. But for some of us, the problem with gardening isn't weeding or sweating, it's overproduction. Just like American agriculture, we're too good at producing crops, so when the onslaught of harvest arrives, supply exceeds demand and we can't get rid of the stuff. All that hard work, just for the compost pile. How depressing. Well, I've changed the way I garden, and it's made me a happier horticulturist.

First, I decided that small is beautiful. No longer do I till up half an acre of ground each spring, sow enough seed for an army, and ignore the fact that I'll be battling weeds, wildlife, and water shortages for the better part of my summer evenings. Instead, I've scaled down big time, from the vast fields of yore to just about 500 square feet. That's only 20 by 25 feet—a horticultural walk in the park. I don't even rototill anymore. My plots are small enough that I simply fork a wheelbarrow full of well-rotted manure into each row before planting, and that's all the tillage required.

Another improvement I've made is to mulch. Instead of bare, scorched earth between rows of vegetables, I now apply a thick layer of straw every few months; this keeps the weeds down and conserves moisture. Makes a nice surface to walk on, too. As it ages it disappears into the soil, adding valuable organic matter, and the few extra field mice that like to live in it don't seem to bother much. On perennial flowers I use gobs of leaf mold.

I get leaves by the truckload from a local landscaper. After a couple of years they're just right for spreading as mulch.

A smaller garden helps control pests, too, especially the four-footed ones; once my vegetable garden was downsized, it was affordable to fence it properly. A tall, sturdy fence keeps out the deer, woodchucks, dogs, and kids. Put up a gate that really works, too. No more tears over lettuce browsed into oblivion by Bambi.

Another bright idea I had was to only grow things I actually like to eat. I'm through with raising long rows of radishes—yuck. Big beds of beet greens, goodbye. And with the deer fenced out, there's nobody to eat the arugula anyway, so adios. Garlic gets a whole row to itself, and that means there must also be plenty of basil to assure an abundant pesto supply. Lots of onions are okay, too, since they keep pretty well in the basement, and a bushel or two of homegrown potatoes won't go to waste in our house.

Some crops I've learned to grow in moderation. I mean, how much zucchini can one family eat, anyway? Turns out that three plants are plenty for us. Since we're too busy, or too lazy, for canning, why grow a hundred tomato plants? I set out a dozen now, all for immediate consumption, half beefsteak and half cherry types. Cucumbers? No more pails of pickles on my to-do list. Six plants of a long, thin-slicing variety meet our salad needs. If I give them a wire fence trellis they grow upward, taking up very little space in the garden.

With more time on my hands, I can fuss over the strawberries. Just fifty plants, two varieties. I weed 'em, I feed 'em, I mulch 'em, I water 'em, and finally I pick 'em. If my garden labor's worth $10 an hour, I figure they only cost me $5 a quart, and it's well worth it to see the kids smile as they pop fresh berries in their mouths. I want their garden memories to be tasty ones.

To get my wife out to the garden, I grow a lot more cut flowers than I used to. She may not like weeding, but she sure likes harvesting a fresh bouquet. All those flowers make the place look nicer, too, although I'm not quite ready for Martha Stewart to visit. There's still that sweat problem. And I think I've got some soil under my fingernails.

Lawn Care

For a few days each spring, you can just about hear the grass growing; it's a horticultural version of ringing in the ears. The conditions that cause it are a week or so of rainy weather followed by the sun coming out and the thermometer going up. Then a botanical time bomb goes off as a million leaves are triggered to lunge upward out of the ground. The brown, flat terrain is transformed into a bright green, three-dimensional landscape of tufted hills and valleys. Shortly thereafter, another reaction occurs across the land, as humans are stricken with an irresistible urge to mow.

I'm not sure whether I mow in order to have a lawn, or if I have a lawn so that I can mow. It's a codependency that could probably be broken with extensive horticultural therapy, but hey, I love to mow ... and I could stop if I wanted to.

A freshly sharpened blade, a full tank of gas, and in a good year, a new spark plug, and we're ready to roll. One pull, two pulls, twenty pulls later the old beast coughs, emits a sideways plume of pollution, and roars to life. I push it onto the field of play and the odor of fossil fuel mingles with the sweet smell of fresh-cut grass.

Lawn care may seem a mindless task to some, but there are important decisions to make right from the get-go. Do I mow the back yard or the front yard first? Should I mow north to south or east to west? Guess I'll just head for where the grass is tallest and go round and round in circles until the unkempt land has been tamed, prettied up by the power of Briggs and Stratton. A sweaty hour later, I look out with satisfaction onto my little patch of the planet where order has been created from chaos, the forces of nature harnessed, and neatness prevails. Oh-oh—in spots where the grass was real thick, I see *imperfections*. Some blades stick up above the others, and there are clumps of unevenly discharged cuttings.

I may have to go back and cut again—perpendicular to the first cut of course, in pursuit of turf utopia, which, by the way, is the infield grass at Fenway Park. Of course, my lawn isn't *that* pampered. No fancy city blue-grasses here, just tough fescues and perennial ryegrasses that can survive in the hills of Vermont. No herbicides either. Instead, I use cultural practices to engage the weeds in mortal combat. First, I apply lime and fertilizer as recommended by a soil test. The grass has to feel good before it can look good. And when it feels good, it grows thicker and faster, competing with weeds for water, light, and nutrients. Then I mow frequently, because that favors plants that can spread sideways, like grasses. Those that cannot, like broadleaf weeds, are cut off at the knees and crowded out.

Most important, I cut the grass high. My mower is set as far up off the ground as it will go, and there it stays. That way, there's always a lot of leaf area for capturing sunlight, which provides the lawn with energy for growth. More leaves, more photosynthesis. Taller grass also competes better with weeds that grow low to the ground. Instead of mowing the grass close, as if shaving, I think of mowing more like trimming a beard.

And finally—I admit it—I pull weeds. Armed with my biggest flathead screwdriver and a five-gallon pail, I spend a few after-dinner hours a year yanking dandelion roots up from China. I know it's a hopeless battle, but, over the long haul, so are herbicides, and I find this technique more satisfying. Besides, I'm making progress, at least in a few spots.

Who cares? you might ask. *What's all the fuss about the lawn?* In rare moments of turf self-doubt, I also question the point of all this work—the energy consumption, the noise, the fumes. Having a lawn is not particularly ecological, but, after all, the kids need a place to run around, we can't have trees growing right next to the house, and the open space creates habitat for deer, field mice, and the neighbor's dogs.

Besides, I ask, can millions of conscientious, grass-cutting Americans *all* be wrong? Just say mow!

Health and History
of Highbush Blueberries

Doctors across the country may soon be prescribing lots of little blue pills, and I don't mean Viagra. They'll be advising patients to eat blueberries, because it turns out that this fruit not only tastes good, it's also good for your health. Researchers have found blueberries to be higher in antioxidants than any other fruit or vegetable tested; by combating free radicals in our bodies, antioxidants help protect against cancer and delay the aging process.

But that's not all. There's also evidence that blueberries can reduce urinary-tract infections and protect against heart disease, too. One study even found that fighter pilots who were given regular doses of blueberries had significantly improved night vision. Could blueberry pancakes someday be classified as a military secret?

Centuries ago, Native Americans knew that blueberries were good for treating stomach problems, but they were limited to eating wild blueberries. Also called lowbush blueberries, these wild plants grow naturally on acid soils, producing fruit that is quite small on plants that only grow about a foot tall. The domesticated or highbush blueberry produces bigger berries, and more of them, on a plant that grows nearly ten times taller than its wild cousin.

The domestication of the blueberry started in 1908, when a researcher at the U.S. Department of Agriculture, Dr. F.V. Coville, began studying wild blueberries and seeking out superior plants for breeding. He made his first selection of plants in New Hampshire. In 1911, he lucked out when Elizabeth White, a commercial cranberry grower in New Jersey, learned of his work and perceived its potential. She offered her assistance, and for the next two decades she enlisted her pickers to search for exceptionally fine blueberry bushes in the wilds of the Pine Barrens. Dr. Coville made crosses among the best of these, and the highbush blueberry industry was eventually born. Coville developed the first fifteen commercial varieties of blueberries, and many more followed as a result of his work.

In 1937, a Vermonter took over the USDA blueberry breeding program. Dr. George Darrow initiated cooperation with state agricultural experiment stations and private growers so that new varieties could be tested in widely different growing conditions. Between 1946 and 1962, he provided over 200,000 seedlings to cooperators in thirteen states. One of these cooperators was his brother Bill, who ran Green Mountain Orchards in Putney.

The first highbush blueberries in Vermont were planted in 1948, Bill Darrow, Jr. told me. "Dad put in thirty or forty bushes at first," he said. "By 1950 he was growing four varieties. He tried different ways of feeding them, and lost quite a few in the process. Eventually he got things squared away, so we cleared the pines off Round Hill, hauled in sawdust from the mill, and planted a couple of acres. We started in 1952, but it took three years to get enough seedlings to finish the planting."

Across town another apple grower, Frank Harlow, was also experimenting with blueberries. "Uncle Frank was a researcher at heart," said Don Harlow, who has grown fruit for fifty years at Harlow's Sugar House. In 1963, Don and his wife Maddy put in their first acre of highbush blueberries, the second commercial planting in the state. Today, both these farms have about fifteen acres of blueberries, and Putney remains the blueberry capital of Vermont.

Elsewhere, word has gotten out about highbush blueberries. They are now grown far and wide, all the way to Japan. Closer to home, 1998 looks to be one of the best blueberry years ever. There's a huge crop in most locations. Pick soon, and pick often. Freezing the berries doesn't diminish their health benefits, so put some up and enjoy them later. A bowl of blueberries a day keeps the doctor away!

Garlic: This Bulb's for You

As the leaves drop from the trees and the growing season comes to an end, my thoughts turn to garlic. Autumn is the time to plant this pungent crop so it will establish its roots before winter sets in, then send up a burst of leaves next spring as soon as the frost is out of the ground. Few vegetables have garnered the attention of farmers, cooks, and health enthusiasts the way garlic has. It's a plant that has been cultivated for thousands of years, and it has some unusual characteristics.

In addition to its unique culinary contribution, garlic offers some remarkable health benefits. Garlic is chock-full of sulfur-containing compounds that provide the plant with its characteristic odor and flavor, and some of these natural chemicals are very effective antibacterial and antifungal agents. In laboratory studies, garlic has been shown to inhibit the growth of two dozen kinds of bacteria, sixty types of fungi and yeast, and it even inactivates certain viruses. The hero appears to be allicin, a stinky sulfur compound that is rapidly formed when garlic is chopped or eaten, but is destroyed when garlic is cooked.

These sulfur compounds probably evolved as a defense mechanism against insect attack. Such odors certainly weren't part of a mating strategy, because garlic has no sexuality. Unlike most other plants, garlic does not produce seeds, so like the potato it is propagated vegetatively. The cloves of the garlic bulb are separated and planted individually; each clove then grows into a new bulb. Fall planting, which is quite unusual among vegetables, is necessary for the proper development of garlic bulbs; exposure to cold temperatures triggers swelling and encourages the bulbs that form the next spring to divide into cloves. For farmers and gardeners, garlic's topsy-turvy production schedule is a break from the regular routine. There's not much else to plant in October, and garlic is harvested at the end of July, before the rush is on to pick other crops.

There are two types of garlic, softneck and topset. Softneck garlic is widely grown in California, Argentina, and China, and this is the garlic usually sold in supermarkets. Softneck garlic bulbs contain a dozen or more small white cloves and, above ground, the plant makes leaves but no flowers.

Topset garlic is the type commonly grown in the Northeast. It's called topset because it produces a tall thin flower stalk, or scape, with a cluster of false flowers at the top. These flowers, instead of making seeds, turn into a ball of tiny bulbils that are another means of vegetative propagation. The underground bulbs formed by topset garlic are great for cooking because they usually contain five to eight large, easy-to-peel cloves, and the flavor is excellent.

There are several farms in Vermont that specialize in growing garlic, and one of these is Yandell Farm in Williston. For the past five years, Hope Yandell has been producing about 1,500 pounds of organic garlic on a third of an acre. "The most I've ever grown is twenty-one varieties of garlic in a single year," she told me. "After a lot of experimenting, I'm down to about a dozen varieties that are well-adapted to my growing conditions. There are literally hundreds of garlic varieties out there, and each has a different flavor, just like apples. The topset types are the true gourmet garlics in terms of flavor, and you can't get them in the supermarket."

Garlic growers are an enthusiastic bunch, and they sponsor a lot of activities. In the Northeast, there are well over a dozen garlic festivals held each year. There's even a quarterly newsletter for garlic growers, *The Garlic Press*, published by the Garlic Seed Foundation. Created fifteen years ago, this nonprofit organization is dedicated to promoting the regional production and consumption of garlic. The Garlic Seed Foundation is run by farmers, and it has over 1,000 members. In addition to its newsletter, the foundation offers books on growing garlic and an annual listing of available seed stock. And the best part is the Garlic Seed Foundation T-shirt that says, "This bulb's for you."

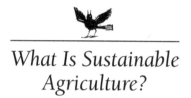

What Is Sustainable Agriculture?

In the Midwest, they know what sustainable agriculture means. Pronounced "stainable agriculture," it's what farming does to your clothes. Back East, where people may drop their rs but not their syllables, there's also some confusion about sustainable agriculture. Is it a communist plot to overthrow agriculture, make all farmers go organic, swear off modern technology, maybe even wear Birkenstocks?

Hardly. Sustainable agriculture is about taking a broader view of what makes farming tick in an effort to find long-term solutions to problems. This holistic way of thinking is becoming more and more widely accepted by bureaucrats, researchers, and farmers. That's significant, because none of these groups is known for easily changing their ways. But, like many other people who love their work, farmers will learn to do many things differently if it means they can stay farmers.

Sustainable agriculture down on the farm means emphasizing ecological management over chemical intervention. Its practitioners try to manage things by using a biological carrot more often than a chemical stick. Off the farm, sustainable agriculture recognizes the connection between healthy farms and strong rural communities. The real definition of sustainable agriculture is simple: Sustainable farms are profitable farms that protect natural resources and are valued by their communities.

The United States Department of Agriculture, after decades of unwittingly promoting high-impact, resource-depleting farming practices, really did an about-face in the late 1980s when, at the request of Congress, they started the Low Input Sustainable Agriculture program, or LISA. This program funded research and education on practices like using cover crops to provide nutrients instead of bagged fertilizers, releasing beneficial organisms to control insects instead of applying pesticides, and promoting intensive pasture management to produce livestock at lower cost with less tillage of the land.

After several years, LISA was renamed SARE, for Sustainable Agriculture Research and Education. The name change came about because simply reducing material inputs doesn't promote sustainability. They must be replaced with a different kind of input—information—if farm productivity is to be maintained. Some folks wanted to rename the program BUBA, for best use of biological applications, but I guess that sounded too macho.

The success of sustainable agriculture practices is judged not only by their effect on yield and profit, but also by their impact on water quality, soil productivity, human health, and the community. That's a big switch from the traditional use of farm output as the sole indicator of success. The catch is that the healthiest long-term practices sometimes yield a little less or may cost a little more up front, even though they pay off over the long haul in terms of more reliable yields and more durable farms. Sustainable ag farmers try to optimize rather than maximize yields, stewarding the resources upon which long-term financial success depends.

Sustainable agriculture is analogous to the practice of human medicine; there's a diversity of opinion about exactly what steps to take in pursuit of good health. The important part is the pursuit itself, not the perfection of a set of instructions. We want doctors and nurses to spend their time healing, not arguing about the definition of health.

Since farming doesn't take place in a vacuum, healthy farming practices must be accompanied by strong markets and supportive public policies that allow for farmers to make a profit. It's ironic that, while more and more researchers and farmers are developing ecologically sound production practices, the social and economic challenges to farming are as serious as ever. To really sustain agriculture in Vermont, we're going to need your help. Obviously, buying local farm products is one thing you can do. But even more important may be supporting tax and land-use policies that recognize we'll be much better off with our farms than without them.

Stonewall Farm and the
Great Pumpkin

I finally got to see the Great Pumpkin. It happened at Stonewall Farm, just outside of Keene, New Hampshire.

Stonewall Farm is an educational center that promotes awareness and appreciation of agriculture and natural resources. Each year over 5,000 children visit the farm to experience barns, gardens, forests, and swamps, and I was there as a chaperone for my son's kindergarten class. The kids were keenly aware that the Great Pumpkin awaited them, but first we had to learn about the things that pumpkins need to grow. The children stood in front of a table full of cucurbits—squashes, gourds, and pumpkins of all sizes and shapes. A jovial and animated educator named Paul led us through songs about vines, flowers, bees, and seeds. He pulled out a box of worms and told us how they helped make the soil better for plant roots to grow in, giving pumpkins, great and small, much happiness.

After a few questions to reinforce the children's newfound knowledge of pumpkin production, we scurried over to the hay wagon. Bonnie and Sam, the farm's team of Belgian draft horses, waited patiently for yet another group of schoolchildren to clamber aboard and settle down. Tiger, the farm manager, dispensed the laws of transportation in classic Cheshire County dialect: No ambiguity, no *r*s, and no hands outside the wagon.

The horses pulled us past chickens, pigs, and goats, the working dairy barn, and pastures full of steadily grazing Holsteins. We saw the late-season remnants of the market garden, and then we entered the forest. Bumping and swaying past a woodland stream and the occasional observation deck, we eventually arrived at our field of dreams. The tension had been building as six-year-olds speculated on the personality of the Great Pumpkin. Would he be friendly? Would he be mean? Given the character of Halloween activities in general, the consensus was that he'd probably be very scary.

The wagon slowed to a halt and the horses were hitched to a fence post. The kids weren't exactly busting at the gate to get off the wagon, so Tiger reassured them that the Great Pumpkin was not someone to be afraid of; in fact, he was so nice that he often gave little kids *a pumpkin of their own to take home*. At this, the energy level soared and everyone bolted to the field where the Great Pumpkin dwelled. When we arrived, he was asleep, and snoring rather loudly. "Hello Great Punkin. Hello Great Punkin!" the little voices shouted. The snoring stopped, a couple of green vines unfolded, and the Great Pumpkin roused himself from a midday nap, grunting and groaning. "Who's there, and what do you want?" he said. He sounded pretty grumpy, so it was a good thing we brought appeasement. "We have some worms for you," the kids said, and one by one they brought an offering and laid it before him. His mood brightened: "Oh thank you, these worms will be very helpful. Say, would you like to pick out a pumpkin from my patch?"

The Great Pumpkin had skin made of orange cloth and his green arms waved about, trailing vinelike strands of fiber. His voice was vaguely familiar; in fact, he sounded a lot like Paul, the fellow we had left back at the cucurbit table not long ago. But no matter—to the kids this was the real thing, the Great Pumpkin in the flesh, and his benevolence and generosity brought relief and excitement. He sang a mean tune, too, and clutching our horticultural loot we joined him in camp songs modified to address the interests of someone who would dress up as a giant cucurbit.

Back on the wagon, pumpkins held between tiny legs swayed to the rhythm of the horses' hooves and pastured turkeys chased after us, hoping for a morsel to eat. Our next activity was lunch, but first there was a slice of pumpkin pie for everyone. Now the kids were *really* impressed: Not only did we got to see the Great Pumpkin, but we got to eat dessert before lunch! This Stonewall Farm is a pretty cool place.

The Value of Vermont's Agriculture

Agriculture holds a special place in the hearts and minds of Vermonters. We know it's important to our state, even if most of us aren't sure exactly why. We live in a global economy now, which means there is inexpensive food from all over the world available in our supermarkets. So what's the real value of agriculture to our state?

Vermont farmers sell over half a billion dollars' worth of products each year, the most of any state in New England. Three-quarters of that amount comes from milk—there's more milk than ever coming from Vermont, and it's being produced by only about 2,000 dairy farms, the fewest in modern history. Dairy farms also produce hay, cattle, Christmas trees, and maple syrup, so the value of their production totally dominates Vermont's agricultural economy.

Yet Vermont's agriculture is also full of surprises. For every dairy farm in Vermont, there are two other farms producing something else; in all, there are about 6,000 farms selling everything from emus to herbs. The largest economic impact of these nondairy enterprises comes from greenhouse and nursery production, which accounts for about 6 percent of total farm sales, followed by vegetables, maple syrup, Christmas trees, and apples, each accounting for just a few percentage points of Vermont's gross agricultural product. Berries, pigs, chickens, eggs, turkeys, and aquaculture each account for less than one percent of farm sales.

In total, nearly a million and a half acres of Vermont's landscape are in agriculture. The value of using land this way is hard to measure, but it is significant. Take tourism for example: It's obvious that agricultural land-scapes and images attract visitors to Vermont. What share of the $2 billion a year that tourists spend can be claimed by agriculture?

The open fields and hedgerows maintained by farming attract not just people but animals, too, enhancing wildlife populations by providing habitat and winter feed. The agricultural terrain also creates opportunities for hunting, hiking, skiing, and snowmobiling; what value do these things have? And, the positive image of the Vermont landscape adds value in the marketplace to everything from specialty foods to teddy bears.

You may be surprised to know that farms save you money. Maintaining undeveloped land keeps property taxes down. When farms are turned into building lots, the demand for infrastructure and services such as schools, roads, and solid waste management increases. One of the conundrums of development is that, even though residential property generates more property tax revenue per acre than farm or forest land, it's not enough to cover the increased cost of community services. The American Farmland Trust looked at studies of forty towns, mostly in the Northeast, that confirm this phenomenon. They found that, on average, farm and forest land costs the towns 31¢ in services, while residential land costs $1.11 for every dollar of property tax generated. There's a saying—"Cows don't go to school, tomatoes don't dial 911"—that's a shortcut way of understanding how community resources are used.

Farms also have value as a source of fresh, wholesome food, available at hundreds of roadside stands, on-farm markets, and farmers' markets. There are also dozens of CSA—community supported agriculture—farms, where members get a weekly box of fresh produce. These direct markets give us access to the farmer as well as to unadulterated and minimally packaged food, without all the advertising and transportation that the rest of our food comes burdened with. Buying direct from the farmer cycles your money within your own community, strengthening the local economy. And, in a region that imports the vast majority of its food, supporting local farms is a way to maintain at least a measure of food security.

Sometimes it's hard to spend a little more to support local agriculture, even when you're aware of all the benefits. But often it's a win-win situation, because the quality of local food is so high. For example, take the eggs I buy at the Brattleboro Co-Op, produced just a couple of miles away on Jay and Janet Bailey's Fairwinds Farm. Sometimes my brain tells me, "Oh my gosh, $2.59 a dozen! I can get eggs for 89¢ at the supermarket." But I buy them anyway, not just because the Baileys are my neighbors, or because their free-running birds are spared a miserable life in a cage, or because their eggs are organically produced. I buy them because they taste better. The same goes for apples and cider from local orchards, local cheeses, local yogurts, local vegetables, and local beer. Well, okay—I concede that beer is not exactly a farm product, but like the rest of the local food it's simply superior.

Vermont's wealth of local food products reflects what is perhaps the most valuable aspect of Vermont's agriculture, and the hardest to quantify: its contribution to our sense of community. Vermont is the most rural state in the nation, in that so many of us live in small towns. The farms in our towns provide us and our neighbors with a sense of place, an identity, and a connection to our land and heritage that is precious. As one farmer once put it, "Vermont without farms could still be a good place, but it could never be Vermont."

Small Farms Are Essential

Maybe you've seen those bumper stickers that say SAVE FAMILY FARMS! Well, I was wondering: Does the secretary of agriculture have one on *his* car? After all, he created a national commission to tell him how to enhance the viability of small farms. That commission spent a year talking to farmers, listening to experts, and analyzing statistics. Then they gave the secretary a report that hits the nail on the head, and it's a good-news, bad-news story.

The good news is that small farms, defined as those with a gross income of a quarter million dollars or less, are alive and kicking—they make up 94 percent of all the farms in this country. They own three-quarters of the productive agricultural assets, mostly land. And because there are so many different kinds of small farms in different places, they contribute to biological diversity and an esthetically pleasing landscape. Small farms also preserve a pattern of decentralized land ownership, and that produces economic opportunity in rural communities.

The bad news is that small farms are at risk. The smallest farms—those with gross sales under $50,000—actually lose money on average. Some of these are hobby farms, but many are real farms, where off-farm income is necessary to keep the family afloat. The biggest of the small farms, those with gross sales between $50,000 and $250,000, spend over 80 percent of what they take in to cover their farming expenses. They end up with an average net income of $23,000 a year.

The title of the commission's report is "A Time to Act." It could have been subtitled, "And This Time We're Not Kidding"; twenty years ago, a similar report was made to the secretary of agriculture, this one called "A Time to Choose." It warned that unless policies promoting ever-larger farming operations were changed, the result would be fewer farms and more corporate control of our food production. Two decades later, it's clear that the warning was not heeded, and that the trend continues toward greater concentration of wealth in farms and agribusinesses.

Today, there are 300,000 fewer farmers than in 1979, and the farmer receives 23¢ of every consumer dollar spent on food. Meanwhile, corporate dominance of our food supply has increased. More farmers than ever work under contract to food-processing firms that want to control the quality and supply of what they buy. For example, 89 percent of all poultry is now produced under contract to food companies, and just four slaughter firms control over 80 percent of the beef market. While contracts in and of themselves are not bad, the reduction in marketplace competition that they foster is one of the strongest forces affecting the viability of small farms.

According to the commission, the food sector of the U.S. economy is second only to the pharmaceutical sector in terms of return on investment, yet the national food economy is structured so that farm families get little of that profit. On the other hand, in local economies, some small farms are thriving, mostly because of direct marketing that cuts out the middleman between farmers and consumers. Across the nation, hundreds of new farmers' markets are started every year, community-supported agriculture is gaining in popularity, and more and more farmers are selling directly to chefs and restaurants. Where direct markets aren't practical, farm cooperatives are starting up to increase the marketing power of small farms with high-quality goods by pooling their products.

The Commission on Small Farms did more than just outline the problems and opportunities that face the majority of our farms; they also compiled a visionary list of public policy changes that would promote family farming, develop fair markets, establish future generations of farmers, and encourage a profitable, ecological, and socially sound agriculture. As consumers, we can support family farms by purchasing their products, and as citizens we can speak out for family farms by urging our politicians to implement the recommendations of the National Commission on Small Farms. Otherwise, the *next* small farm report may be titled "A Time to Remember."

1999

Nolan Farm Celebration

It was almost Independence Day and I was going to a celebration; people were gathering to cheer the preservation of a beautiful and productive piece of land in West Arlington, Vermont. Known as the Vaughn Farm, this property stretched along the Battenkill River at the bottom of a lush valley not far from the New York border. As I drove over the covered bridge that leads to the farm, I was excited. There was a whiff of revolution in the air.

When I first visited this farm a couple of years ago, it was in my role as a vegetable extension agent. Judy and John Nolan were renting the farm. At first they had tried to keep it going as a small dairy, and then they had switched to growing vegetables, sweet corn, and hay. It was spring, and Judy had some sick pepper plants in the greenhouse. She gave me a call and I came to look them over. Although I couldn't offer much useful advice, she invited me in for a tuna sandwich anyway. Over lunch I pried into things that are none of my business, as extension agents sometimes do, and she told me about their lease situation, and how much she and John hoped to work something out so they could eventually own the farm and stay there.

It turned out that the owner, Clare Vaughn, a woman getting on in years, wanted to make sure that her farm didn't get developed—ever. To achieve this, she started working with the Vermont Land Trust, which arranged for a conservation easement on the farm by purchasing the development rights. This easement will keep the land open and will lower the price of the farm on the real-estate market, which also brings the Nolans one step closer to realizing their dream of farm ownership. To achieve that dream, they are working incredibly hard. Judy grows vegetables for a community supported agriculture program with a membership of two dozen families, while John grows twenty acres of sweet corn for sale to local supermarkets. On top of that, like many other farmers, they both have full-time jobs off the farm.

I think of the Nolans and thousands of other Vermont farmers like them as revolutionaries: They are modern-day Minutemen and -women fighting a war for control of our food system. Outgunned by well-financed food conglomerates, which are the British, and discriminated against by government policies that favor industrial agriculture, which are the taxes on teas and commerce, they have chosen to rise up against those who have imposed on us a system of cheap, uniform food from distant ports, made inexpensive by indirect subsidies of water and transportation, and all of it supported by a research infrastructure that promotes chemical inputs and genetic engineering over local ecosystem knowledge and long-term stewardship of natural resources. Aided by land trusts and agricultural organizations, who are the French and sympathetic Native Americans, this new breed of Minuteman is helping Vermont to boldly go where no state has gone before, to seek out the nooks and crannies of the food system that let farmers receive a fair price for their product while offering consumers a chance to vote with their dollars about the kind of landscape and the type of food they want.

This revolution can be seen in the steady growth of community supported agriculture, farmers' markets, food co-ops, roadside stands, and farmstead cheeses, yogurts, and meats. You can also see this revolution in action when restaurants seek out local food products and Vermont specialty food producers, acting on their commitment to buying Vermont-grown ingredients. There's still a long way to go to agricultural independence and equal rights for small farms in Vermont, but we can get there—one farm, one farm family, and one set of loyal customers at a time.

Safe Food:
Where Does It Come From?

I've decided to change what I eat. No more fresh fruits or vegetables, they're *just too dangerous!* I'm sticking to Twinkies, Spam, and Froot Loops—that ought to be a safe diet. You see, those scary stories in the media have me concerned that there may be microbes in the food I eat. If I get any more worried, I'm going to start buying freeze-dried army rations.

Of course, I won't be eating any organic food, since some people say it's particularly dangerous: Organic farmers use *manure* to fertilize the soil. Never mind that this practice is as old as civilization, commonly employed on nonorganic farms, and that manure is an invaluable soil amendment that doesn't come in contact with food if it's properly managed. Still, I prefer chemically fertilized, irradiated, processed, vacuum-packed *health* food. And did I mention that I wash my hands with antibacterial soap before and after every meal?

Okay, that's enough sarcasm. Food safety *is* an important issue, and there *are* some dangerous organisms that can flourish in food if it's improperly produced or handled. The issue of food safety has gained public attention because of the relatively few times that products have become contaminated with bacteria like *E. coli* or salmonella. These incidents have dramatically heightened attention to sanitary practices on farms, at food processing plants, in restaurants, and in kitchens like yours. And that's a good thing, because a safe food system requires that everyone, from farmers to consumers, take responsibility for handling food properly. But, on the other hand, media attention and aggressive public health responses to food safety can cause hardships to farmers that may be unwarranted. Take apple cider, for example.

A few years ago, several people in the western United States got sick and a child even died from E. coli poisoning after drinking fresh-squeezed juice. As a result, all fresh juices became suspect, and now it's just about impossible for Vermont apple-cider makers to sell their product to supermarkets unless it's pasteurized. That requires expensive equipment, so many small cider makers have gone out of business. Those that continue to sell fresh, unpasteurized cider are required to label their containers to say that cider may be dangerous to consume, especially for kids and the elderly. All this because a few producers did not take the care to assure that their product had not come in contact with animal feces.

Given that there's no evidence that apple cider made from sound, thoroughly washed fruit ever made anyone sick here in Vermont, one farmer has proposed an alternative label. It would say, THIS CIDER IS CHOCK-FULL OF MICRO-ORGANISMS THAT WILL HELP YOU LIVE A LONG AND HEALTHY LIFE.

That was a joke, but it underscores a fundamental choice in matters of food safety. We can attempt to sterilize farms and their products, and we can live in fear of any life in our food. Or we can have policies and educational programs that help food producers, processors, and consumers practice cleanliness and be individually accountable for the safety of their products.

Right now, people get most of their food from nobody-knows-where; much of it comes from large factories that mix raw ingredients from many locations, process them, and ship the output all over the continent. If someone gets sick there are recalls, legal fees, and corporate fines, but no person is really responsible. By patronizing small-scale farmers and processors, consumers have the opportunity to look the food producer in the eye at farmers' market, see their name on the label at the store, or visit the farm or facility where the product comes from. Fresh food, grown close to home and processed in clean facilities by knowledgeable handlers—that's the kind of food safety program I want. Until then, pass the Twinkies, please.

A Prison Visit

I knew right away this wasn't going to be an ordinary extension farm visit, perhaps because there was razor wire around the fields, uniformed guards, and a metal detector. But what did I expect? I was visiting some unusual farmers, all of them inmates at the Northwest Region Correctional Facility in St. Albans, Vermont.

It took me several tries to make it through the metal detector. After removing my keys, coins, belt, and wedding ring I finally succeeded. I signed in, got a visitor ID, and had my briefcase searched. Then I was escorted through a double set of remote-controlled locked doors and out into the prison yard. There, beyond the basketball court and the exercise area, were vegetables—lots of them. Dozens and dozens of rows of tomatoes, carefully tied and staked. Potatoes, beets, chard, and melons were in neat plots, and many plots were already harvested. In these, a cover crop of oats was knee-high in some places, and between the rows of remaining vegetables were well-trimmed strips of white clover. The evidence of horticultural skill and stewardship was abundant, and so was the metal fencing.

In a small classroom I met with the handful of men who had volunteered to work the six acres of vegetables on the prison grounds. These inmates were polite, enthusiastic, and proud of what they had accomplished in the fields. There were a lot of questions about soil fertility and organic pest control, which I did my best to answer. The men told me how much they enjoyed growing vegetables. It gave them the opportunity to get away from their regular routines, and to give something back to the community.

I'd been invited to visit the prison and give some vegetable-growing advice by Liz Hall, director of Community Action in Franklin and Grand Isle counties. Her office coordinates emergency services for low-income people, and it was her idea to work with the prison to grow organic produce for people who need food. While some of the vegetables are used in the prison cafeteria, most of the crops get distributed through Community Action emergency food shelves. Before I left, I watched the men load a pickup truck with boxes of onions, carrots, potatoes, and squash they had just picked.

This is clearly a win-win project, providing a healthy activity for inmates while producing tens of thousands of pounds of fresh food for the community. Of course, the project wouldn't work without the involvement of some special people. Rebecca Moyer is a part-time garlic farmer who works at Community Action and coordinates the program. To help her manage the field work, she hired Rona Cohen, who has been an organic farmer in Vermont for twenty years. The rapport that these women have with the prisoners is impressive. There's obviously a lot of mutual respect, and they all manage to enjoy the work, too. But everyone knows the rules, which are strict.

There are only certain hours when the men can be out in the fields. No dangerous equipment is allowed. Tall crops like sweet corn are prohibited, because a person could hide in them. And black plastic mulch isn't allowed because it might be fashioned into a rope that could be used for an escape attempt.

These are not the only constraints the project faces. There is no tractor, nor is there a greenhouse, and there's not much money for the purchase of fertilizers, compost, or seeds. Thankfully, the Community High School of Vermont and the Vermont Department of Corrections are extremely supportive of the project and allocate some funding to keep it going. Generous donations from nearby Hudak Farm, Hamlin's Greenhouse, and the Mississquoi Valley High School provide the prison with thousands of seedlings each spring.

A Beaver Pond
Just up the Road

You could hear the peepers a quarter-mile away. My five-year-old's face lit up, and he whispered, "We better be quiet so we don't scare them."

"I *am* quiet!" shouted my two-year-old, and we continued our walk up the overgrown logging road to the beaver pond at the top of the hill. Still, a quarter-mile is a long way for a child to remember to be quiet, and there was a hardly a peep out of the nervous peepers by the time we arrived. We crouched by the edge of the slimy broth of the pond, leaning on a large tree the beavers had recently felled. All eyes were on the water; fish nets were firmly clasped in little hands, poised for action. Suddenly there was a bubble and wiggle in the water and the swoosh of a net. "I got it, I got it!" "Lemme see, lemme see!"

At the bottom of the net, along with a healthy serving of muck and leaves, was our unsuspecting prey: an Eastern newt. The poor guy was in for quite an experience, since he was about to be nearly loved to death by two little boys. "It's my turn, lemme hold it," "No, I caught it—it's mine." Squeals of delight mingled with cries of competition as the newt was passed back and forth a dozen times; it slipped away once or twice, only to be gathered up by four hands at once.

"Okay, that's enough," I said. "Put him back before he gets hurt." The newt was tenderly dropped from a height of several feet back into the pond, and for a while he just floated in place, totally exhausted.

"Daddy, can we catch him again?"

"That would be cheating," I said. "Look how tired he is. Let's go find another one." Relieved to see our victim swim off, we moved to another prime hunting ground.

By now the peepers were growing accustomed to our presence and slowly but steadily cranking up the volume, eventually reaching their former decibel level, which at close range was just about earsplitting. High peeps, low peeps, fast peeps, slow peeps. Froggy went a courtin', big time. The crazy thing, of course, is that there wasn't a frog to be seen.

We hauled in another four or five newts, along with various leeches, aquatic insects, and piles of goop that had produced bubbles but on close examination showed no visible signs of life. Now came the hard part—it was time to go home. "Just a few more minutes? One more newt Daddy, okay?" The boys had not yet reached their personal slime quota, and someone would either have to fall in or at least get pond water in their boots before departure would be an acceptable idea.

Walking down the hill we came out of the woods and into civilization, passing a few small summer camps, an old house there, a new house here. How long, I wondered, before development creeps up the logging road and the beaver pond no longer feels like wilderness but more like someone's backyard?

That night our town had a public meeting about a proposal to manage growth in the town. The planning commission was looking for a way to reduce the potential for the widespread subdivision of land, yet still allow people to develop their property. Ideas on the table included sliding-scale zoning, which would leave some land open when large properties were divided up, and cluster zoning, which would lower the required minimum lot size in exchange for keeping the majority of a big parcel undeveloped.

At the meeting there was a lot of angry reaction. "You'll lower the value of my property because I can't sell as many lots," said one man. "This will raise our taxes and create an elite community of high-value homes," said another. "If it ain't broke, don't fix it," a chorus rang out. A few others applauded the proposal, saying they valued the rural character of our town and wanted it protected.

Since extensive development is not yet in our faces, and because our town is still very rural, it's hard for people to plan for growth over the long haul. But that's what is needed if we want our kids and their kids to have a rural town, too. If you think about what's coming at us over the next ten, twenty, or fifty years, as more and more people move to the country, free to conduct their business via phone, fax, and the Internet, you may hear the call to action. And if you think implementing a plan to maintain open land is difficult now, just wait till the onslaught is in full swing, and everybody wants a beaver pond in their backyard.

Public Servant Stories

The stories you are about to hear are true, but the names have been changed to protect the innocent, namely me. You see, I work for University of Vermont Extension, and I answer the phone. These are tales of close encounters with inquiring minds.

Extension is the outreach arm of the university. We provide training and information on practical topics from apple production to water quality. A lot of people come to extension looking for answers. Surveys shows that half of all Vermonters have contacted extension at one time or another and, as an agriculture specialist, I get my fair share of calls. Some of them are real doozies.

"Hello, I'd like to report a grape," the caller said.

I paused. What was the proper response? "Good..." I said. It's not easy being a public servant, especially if you tend toward the sarcastic. I was thinking of places the caller could put that grape. "How can I help?"

"Well, it's a really big grape, biggest one I've ever seen, and I want to know where to send it to be examined."

My mind raced. Department of Agriculture? The Smithsonian? Guinness Book of World Records? I needed more information. "Where did you find this big grape?"

"In the supermarket!"

"Oh. And why do you want it examined?"

"Well, it could be used by scientists to breed bigger grapes."

At this point I explained that, as I understood it, a single grape, especially a seedless one, was probably not going to be very useful to plant breeders, but thanks for calling anyway.

Then there was the little old lady and her bird feeder. I had just started working for extension, and I really didn't know what I was in for. "I've got this bird bath," she said. "It's made from an upside-down garbage-can lid, mounted on a post. I painted the lid black to keep the water warm, but now the paint is peeling off and I want to know if it'll hurt the birds."

Hmm. I had expected questions about fertilizing blueberries or controlling insect pests. I really wasn't trained to take this kind of abuse. "Well, gee," I stalled, "I really don't know." Suddenly, an inspiration. "Say, why don't you use a *plastic* garbage can lid instead—a dark colored one—and then you won't have to paint it."

"Oh what a good idea. Thank you *so much.*"

I love it when they go away happy.

But sometimes they don't go away happy, even when I offer good advice. "There's bugs all over my house," the man yelled. "Been there for days. I just threw gasoline on 'em to kill 'em, but I want to know what they are."

"Sir, you *really* shouldn't be throwing gasoline around your house. Bad idea. Bring a few bugs down to the office and we'll send them off for identification and figure out what to do."

"Can't wait that long, they're everywhere, just tell me what they are."

And I'm thinking, *I hope you're not a smoker.*

Other calls that make me nervous are about poisonous plants: "Hello. There's a big bush in my yard with lots of little red berries on it and I wanted to know if they're dangerous to eat."

"Better safe than sorry," I say. "I wouldn't suggest eating them."

"Well, I run a day care and the kids play under the bush and pick the berries all the time."

Oh-oh. "If you bring the plant in I'll try to identify it." I say. "But in the meantime, I'd keep the kids away from it."

The receptionist buzzes me. "There's someone on the phone who has just bought a farm," she says.

Oh good, I think. *A normal phone call, probably about soil tests, or building a greenhouse.*

"What can I grow in Vermont to make money?" the caller asks.

Ah, another aspiring farmer seeking the wrong answers. I respond gently: "You can grow just about anything in Vermont. A better question might be what can you sell at a profit that you have the resources and interest to produce." This leads to a long conversation about setting goals, market research, and consumer trends. *A flash in the pan?* I wonder. *Or will this one follow through?* I hope he does, that he joins the ranks of Vermont farmers producing and processing all kinds of products.

The day is winding down, and the voice-mail, e-mail, and snail-mail inquiries are all answered, some better than others. It's time for this extension agent to head home, where more difficult questions await, like "Daddy, what's for dinner?"

Transgenic Crops:
A Cause for Concern

From our safe haven in Vermont, it seems like all the fuss over agricultural biotechnology is just so much hype—on both sides. After all, how could a few genes spliced here and there lead to the salvation, or to the meltdown, of the world's food system?

Those who stand to benefit professionally and financially are touting the benefits of transgenic crops, which are crops with genes from other organisms spliced into their DNA. These new crops will help feed the hungry, they say, and reduce the need for pesticides in agriculture. Others are questioning the risks associated with genetically modified crops and asking who really benefits from their development. These questions are no joke, especially since the cat is well out of the bag. In recent years the application of transgenic crops down on the farm has been incredibly rapid and widespread, largely due to the efforts of a few large corporations.

There are now dozens of commercially available transgenic crop varieties, mostly in soybean, corn, cotton, and canola, although vegetables and fruits are coming on line, too. Worldwide, there were 70 million acres of transgenic crops planted in 1998, and 51 million of these were in the U.S., more than double the acreage we grew the year before. The vast majority of these crops contains one of two traits: herbicide or insect resistance.

For example, so-called RoundUp-ready crops have been genetically engineered to resist the herbicide glyphosate, known as RoundUp. Farmers can spray this herbicide right over the resistant crops to get rid of the weeds without killing the crop. This sounds good in theory, but of course the farmers will have to depend on one supplier for both their seed and their herbicide. And so long to crop rotation and mechanical cultivation for weed control. It's likely that, in a few years, most of the corn and soybeans in this country will be RoundUp ready. Soon after that, the supermarkets will likely be stocked with RoundUp-ready lettuce and strawberries, too.

Other transgenic varieties of cotton, corn, and potatoes have been bioengineered to resist insects. Most of these contain a gene from a bacterium called *Bacillus thuringiensis,* or *B.t.* Insecticides containing *B.t.* have been used for many years to control leaf-eating caterpillars. The most widely-used biological pesticide in the world, *B.t.* is safe and effective, and it's an important tool for organic farmers. Normally, when *B.t.* is sprayed on crops, most but not all of the pests are killed; some of them always get away. But when the *B.t.* toxin is built right into the crops, every bite that every pest takes contains *B.t.*, so only those that can tolerate it will survive. These survivors reproduce, creating a population that is resistant to *B.t.* in any form. Many farmers and scientists fear that in a few years we can kiss *B.t.* goodbye.

With all this good stuff in the new crops, at a cost of tens of billions dollars, farmers are not allowed to save their own seed and bypass corporate profits. That seems fair enough. But just to be sure, another genetic modification has been invented called the Terminator gene. It causes otherwise viable seeds to be sterile, and thus worthless to farmers. Incredible as it sounds, this gene was developed with the assistance of the U.S. Department of Agriculture, and it's now owned by Monsanto. Terminator technology may eventually be added to many crops. This is no big deal for farmers who plant hybrids anyway, and don't save their own seed, but if Terminator is put into open-pollinated varieties, farmers will be denied the time-honored practice of saving their own seeds. In poor countries, this could cause real economic hardship.

The scary part of all this is the potential for unanticipated ecosystem effects such as genetic pollution from transgenic crops. To what extent can pollen from genetically modified crops spread from the fields where they are planted and fertilize their nonengineered cousins? Will herbicide resistance, insecticidal leaves, and sterile seeds turn up in places we don't want them? And how will a regular diet of transgenic crops affect the creatures that eat them, including we humans? Although far too few studies are looking at these issues, there are reports of declines in insect reproduction and of a reduction in the size of mammalian organs when genetically modified plants are consumed.

In Europe, there's a groundswell of opposition to genetically engineered food among people and governments. Here, there are fewer voices asking whether corporate promotion and control of biotechnology should be allowed such free rein when so many important questions remain unanswered. Nature has served us well, even when we tinkered with it and started farming. Now we presume to improve on nature at an unprecedented pace in the name of short-term corporate profit rather than ecological or economic sustainability. It seems to me that we're biting the hand that feeds us, and it will slap us down unless we show some respect.

Organic Farming
in Vermont

Over the past few years, sales of organic products have been increasing by about 20 percent annually, fueled by rising consumer interest in healthy food and environmental stewardship. Organic certification is a process designed to ensure that consumers really get what they pay for when they buy organic. There are dozens of organizations that run certification programs, and, in the United States, most of these programs cover a single state. In Vermont, the Northeast Organic Farming Association, or NOFA, has provided a program for verification of organic food production and processing since 1985. The certification committee of NOFA is called the Vermont Organic Farmers, and last year the program certified 158 organic farms and twenty-two organic processors. That represents about 15,000 acres of land across the state in organic production and $25 million in sales. This year, NOFA anticipates that 200 farms will be certified organic, more than double the number just five years ago.

Organic standards are the basis of certification programs, since they define which techniques and materials can or can't be used to produce organic food. While there are differences among the standards of various certification programs, in general they are minor, and all certification programs seek to promote a system of food production that biologically enhances soil, plant, and animal life.

To become certified in Vermont, a farmer must submit an initial application that describes the management history of the farm's soils, crops, and pests over the past three years, as well current plans for crop and animal production. A signed and notarized affidavit is required, testifying to the truth of the information provided. To maintain certification in subsequent years, an annual application must be submitted that documents the farm's adherence to the organic standards. Each year, a committee reviews the applications, and then field inspectors visit every farm that applies for certification, spending several hours on site to verify the information submitted. Inspectors also assist with problem-solving related to organic production.

To get certified, farmers pay an annual fee ranging from $150 to $550, based on their gross sales of organic products. This can be an economic burden for farmers, but the fees barely cover the costs of running NOFA's certification program.

To be approved for organic certification, a farm must document that no prohibited pesticides or fertilizers were applied during the three years prior to crop harvest. Dairy farms must document that their animals have been managed in accordance with organic standards for at least a year before selling milk or dairy products as organic.

Like all farms, organic farms have pests to deal with. Organic standards allow the use of pest-management tools such as crop rotation, insect predators and parasites, and mechanical cultivation. Applying botanical insecticides or using plastic mulch for weed control is permitted but it's not encouraged.

To keep organic animals healthy, preventive management is used, with a focus on building healthy soils in order to produce high-quality feed. If animals get sick, farmers are permitted to use homeopathic and other natural remedies. In a veterinary emergency conventional medication may be used, but this is followed by an extended withholding period before the milk from that animal can be sold again as organic.

Soil fertility on organic farms is maintained by growing green manures such as clover and alfalfa, and by adding nutrients as needed in the form of naturally occurring minerals like limestone and rock phosphate. Compost is widely used on organic farms, but raw manure is not allowed to be added to the soil less than six weeks prior to harvesting a food crop.

Organic standards also cover post-harvest handling and processing of food, meat and egg production, animal housing, and other aspects of farm management. These standards have been worked out over the years by organic farmers themselves, with them often putting in many hours in the winter to resolve complicated issues. The result is a certification program that protects the integrity of the organic label, provides consumer assurance, and allows for a workable system of production for farmers and processors.

The Two Trains
of Agriculture

I n the distance I can hear the whistles blowing. One is a sweet melody in harmony with the sounds of the night, and the other is a powerful blast of noise, disturbing anything in its way. The sounds come from the two trains on the tracks of agriculture today, trains that are going in opposite directions.

One train is the Industrial Agriculture Express, which consumes great quantities of natural resources as it speeds ahead toward a cheap, uniform food supply. Its engine is powered by fewer and fewer farms that rely more and more on inputs of chemicals, genetically engineered organisms, hormones, irradiation, and other technologies designed to yield profits for corporations.

The other train is the Sustainable Agriculture Local, which plods slowly but steadily along, carefully conserving the resources it needs to produce fresh, healthy products in season. Its engine is fueled by local farms that rely heavily on biological inputs, providing regional food security, economic benefits to nearby communities, and opportunities for farmers to make a decent living while stewarding the land.

If you read the newspaper on the Industrial Agriculture Express, you'll find it is full of bad news. Genetically engineered crops, almost unheard of a decade ago, are now grown on tens of millions of acres, mostly in this country. Just five corporations sell nearly all the seed for these crops. The same five corporations also sell two-thirds of all the pesticides in the world. In the United States alone, that's over a billion pounds of pesticide a year.

These same five corporations have also been buying up seed companies, and now control a quarter of all the commercial seeds available worldwide. And while food is cheap in this country, its quality is questionable. Year in and year out, the government finds that two-thirds of the fresh produce sampled from the marketplace have low levels of pesticide residues. We consume this food because the low levels are legal. We're also consuming genetically engineered products, but we don't know when. Foods that contain soy, corn, or canola are likely to be made with genetically engineered crops, but since labeling isn't required, consumers in this country have no way of knowing. And finally, the farmers who work so hard to grow the food we eat are a dying breed. In 1959 there were six million farms in the U.S.; now there are two million.

On the Sustainable Agriculture Local, there is plenty of good news in the paper. Many farmers are bypassing the distributors and processors that gobble up their profits and instead are marketing directly to consumers, or making their own value-added products. Sales of organic foods continue to grow by 20 percent annually. Last year 280,000 people let the U.S. Department of Agriculture know that they don't want the quality of certified organic food to be compromised. Supermarkets are starting to recognize farmers for using integrated pest management, or IPM, which reduces unnecessary pesticide applications. Some mainstream agricultural researchers are taking up the study of agricultural ecology, discovering wonderful things such as natural responses by plants that ward off insect pests. And, thankfully, there are still many young people who would like to become farmers, if they can find a way to get started and make a decent living.

Although industrial agriculture has a lot of political and economic power, sustainable agriculture offers many more benefits for the consuming public. You can help shape the future of agriculture—buy a ticket on the right train by using your food dollars to cast a vote for sustainability. Buy local, buy organic, buy IPM. Let your legislators know what kind of food system you want. Ask for labeling of genetically engineered foods, insist on policies that are fair to small farms, and plead for publicly funded research that supports ecological farming. Or you can just sit back and get taken for a ride.

2000

Neutrality,
in My Opinion

W here *is* that line? If only I could see it, maybe I'd stop stepping over it. Ten years ago, when I started in Cooperative Extension, the line was clear to me. My job was to offer unbiased, research-based information about agriculture. Just the facts. Opinions were out of bounds. It seemed simple enough, and it made sense, especially when the questions I fielded stayed in the ballpark. There were pop flies like *How much fertilizer does sweet corn need?* and the occasional line drive like *Where can I sell these crops?* But then along came the heavy hitters with queries that weren't readily addressed by a neat set of data. Questions like *How do I get along with my nonfarming neighbors? And What's the value of agriculture?* Or, lately, *Should I plant genetically engineered crops?*

Agriculture, along with the rest of society, is increasingly faced with complex issues that don't lend themselves to a black-and-white interpretation. And while there's scientific data about these complex issues, it tends to come from studies that address small components of big questions. Often the data from different studies is contradictory and its ultimate meaning in terms of any big-picture conclusions requires subjective analysis. If that's the case, does it make sense for extension educators and scientists to continue to struggle valiantly to maintain a neutral position, answering controversial questions with on-the-one-hand-this, on-the-other-hand-that replies? Or would it serve the public interest better if we summarize what appears to be the facts and then, in addition, offer a professional but personal interpretation that *does* take a position but *doesn't* speak for the institutions that employ us?

Many of the farmers I work with want more than a list of pros and cons when they face a tough decision. They ask me, "What do *you* think?" And they want a straight answer. Historically, providers of so-called neutral information *have* been giving them answers—professional opinions based on the facts as they saw them: "Spray that DDT." And "Spread that phosphorus fertilizer," and "Build those tall blue silos," and "Get big or get out."

Providing a professional opinion can be dangerous, because sometimes you'll be proven wrong and most times you'll make someone mad. But coping with complex issues requires an honest and civil exchange of opinions by citizens and public servants alike, whether we're talking about genetically modified organisms, industrial-scale farming, or public policies that affect the agricultural marketplace. Clearly we need to keep facts separate from opinions, but we also need to admit that there is no way to draw completely objective conclusions about controversial issues. Even scientific data is affected by bias, since the questions that researchers choose to study are often those that interest them personally. The public deserves an airing of diverse opinions based on reasoned interpretations of the evidence.

So when I say that I'm concerned about the long-term effects of genetically modified crops on the ecosystem and on the economic viability of farms, I am giving you my carefully considered opinion based on the data I've seen. I am not speaking for UVM or for the USDA, although I am employed by these institutions, and I acknowledge that there are other interpretations of the data, and that many scientists and public officials do not share my concern.

But given my concern, and given the magnitude of this issue, I feel a responsibility to admit what I think, especially when the public may be ill-informed about the potential consequences of emerging technologies. The only way for people to avoid an outcome they don't desire is to learn more about the issues and take their own stand before irreversible damage is done. Encouraging and informing this debate is, in my opinion, a real public service.

Land Link Vermont:
Keeping Farmland in Production

I stepped to the podium and broke into a sweat. My heart pounded as the realization hit me—I was in the wrong place! There was a sea of gray hair before me. I was supposed to be speaking to vegetable growers at an extension workshop. Where were they?

Then it dawned on me. I *was* in the right place, but at the wrong time. This audience, with an average age of about sixty-five, *was* full of vegetable growers. I had traveled four hours to talk about organic farming, but I was forty years too late. And despite the fact that the meeting focused on techniques for growing crops, these farmers had more important concerns.

At lunch, I sat with the youngsters: Fifty-something sons and grandsons of farmers whose families have worked the fertile plain of southeastern New Hampshire for generations. They talked about the future of their farms. Sprawl, high property taxes, escalating land values, new regulations, and the lack of reliable labor were the topics on the table. Sure, we chatted about varieties and irrigation, but that was just for comic relief.

Everyone knows that farming can be a challenge, but it's especially difficult in places where there are lots of people, lots of suburban growth, and lots of competing demands for good land. My lunch mates told stories about a way of life under siege. They had siblings who were pressuring them to sell out, given the fortune that their land was worth for nonagricultural uses. There were offers from developers that came all too often, with far too many zeros. There were ongoing battles with local tax assessors, who were punishing these farmers for having rich neighbors. Employees were gone just about as fast as you could hire them, and fights with the state were looming over water rights for irrigation and the ability to use pesticides.

Yet, for the most part, these farmers were going to keep right on doing what they love doing. And if someone competent wants to take over the farm when they're ready to retire, why they'll bend over backwards to make it happen. The good news is that there *are* people looking for farms. Some of them are young and inexperienced, but others have many years of farming under their belts. Still others are career-changers, with business experience, capital, and the willingness to obtain the information they'll need to succeed.

Of course the retiring and the aspiring farmers don't always hook up. Too often, farmers don't make plans for the future until they want to—or have to—stop farming. Then they sell the property on the open market, which often means the land is converted to nonfarm uses and which leaves them with a big tax bill. And in many cases, those looking for farmland are not in a position to actually buy it, given the high cost.

Ideally, these obstacles to farmland transfer can be overcome. Creative arrangements between farm seekers and farm sellers can allow for a gradual transfer of property that is mutually acceptable and economically practical. These arrangements can include things like leasing, partnerships, or the purchase of equipment and buildings but rental of the land. These approaches allow a seeker with limited funds to get on the land, while still allowing the landowner to both make money from their property and keep it in farming.

At the UVM Center for Sustainable Agriculture, we've started a program called Land Link Vermont to help keep land in agriculture. The program provides education about alternative land transfer arrangements, as well as a matching service between people that are seeking land to farm and those with farmland to sell, lease, or share.

Revised Organic Standards

Organic food is big business. The USDA, the United States Department of Agriculture, says that retail sales of organic foods totaled $6 billion last year. There are over 12,000 organic farms across the country, and that number is rising by 12 percent a year. And there are forty-nine different organizations and agencies that certify organic farms. The time is at hand to establish a uniform set of organic standards, but it's easier said than done.

In 1990, Congress called for a national organic certification program. Since then, the USDA has been developing the rules for that program, and they came up with a first draft in 1997. In response to those draft rules, they got their largest public feedback ever: Over 275,000 people sent in their comments, and these people almost universally objected to the proposed rules. This past March, the USDA tried again.

The second draft of the rules prohibits the use of genetic engineering, sewage sludge, and irradiation in the production of organic foods, and many other changes were made in response to comments from the public. The USDA deserves credit for formulating a much-improved set of rules. And although many people worry that a federally administered organic program will be nothing but trouble, well, the cat's out of the bag, and I doubt it can be put back in, so the best tactic may be to try and get along with it.

The new proposed rules prohibit the use of most synthetic pesticides and fertilizers for at least three years before the harvest of an organic crop.

They also prohibit the continuous confinement of animals and require crop rotation and the least-toxic pest-management methods. They further specify what kinds of microbial, botanical, and nontoxic man-made pesticides can be used.

Under the rules, farms that sell more than $5,000 worth of food labeled as organic must be certified by a USDA-accredited agent. The USDA will make the rules, but the certifying agents will inspect the farms and have the authority to decertify those that don't comply with them.

The proposed rules for labeling of organic foods are a bit complicated, so you might want to get out your calculators. Products made entirely with certified organic ingredients may be labeled *100 percent organic*; products containing at least 95 percent certified organic ingredients may be labeled simply *organic*, and products containing at least 50 percent certified organic ingredients may be labeled *made with organic ingredients*. If a product contains less than 50 percent certified organic ingredients it can't be labeled organic at all, but the organic ingredients can be listed in the ingredients statement.

A longtime organic farmer told me what he thinks of the government's program. "They have the whole thing backwards. It's the *consumer* who needs certification. Do you smoke? Do you drink? How much fossil fuel do you burn, and how much do you recycle? Only the people with the healthiest lifestyle should be eligible to purchase organic food."

Environmental Circumscription

I thought I was immune, but it happened: I came down with a bad case of road rage while I was driving to Boston with the kids. As we approached the city, it seemed that cars came out of nowhere, and suddenly it was bumper-to-bumper at 70 miles an hour for as far as the eye could see. That's when I saw *him*. Suit and tie, cell phone in hand, he was bobbing and weaving his vehicle dangerously through the traffic. *He* didn't have road rage, but he was a carrier. He squeezed in front of me with barely a foot to spare and hit the brakes.

The profanities spewed forth: "Gee whillikers!" I exclaimed—this is the kind of silly expletive you use when children are around. After my outburst we continued along in our lane while the offender maneuvered back and forth among the cars ahead of us. Soon he was out of sight. But ten minutes later, there he was again. Like a recurring bad dream, he swerved in front of us, then jammed on the brakes. We nearly collided. I had no verbal options left, since silly expletives would no longer do. My lips moved but nothing came out. I shook my fist in the air. Then I glanced in the rearview mirror. Two little pairs of eyes looked back at me with curiosity. I could read their thoughts: "Right now, Daddy's elevator doesn't go all the way to the top."

My heartbeat returned to normal and my thoughts circled around what had just happened. What made a person risk life and limb to gain such a slight advantage? How can someone who's probably quite normal in other situations get so aggressive? My memory unearthed an anthropology course

I took in college where we watched a film about a tribe that lived in the rain forest. Most of the time they hunted, gathered, or just hung out. On special occasions they consumed hallucinogenic beans, which was a real hoot when the anthropologists came by to collect stool samples in test tubes. But every once in a while they painted themselves to look ferocious and they went to war. Why?

It wasn't for money, and it wasn't for politics. Instead, it was because of what's been called *environmental circumscription*, or having too many people in too small a space. When the population got cramped, the men paid a hostile visit to the neighboring tribe and intimidated them into moving away. Suddenly, interstate traffic made sense to me!

Have you ever noticed how drivers are relatively rational when they're few and far between, like on the stretch of I-89 between White River and Montpelier? But the closer you get to Burlington, where the population is denser, the more aggressive the driving becomes. And if you venture south down I-91, it's a relaxing trip all the way into northern Massachusetts, but once you're near big cities like Holyoke or Hartford, people get crazy.

This connection between population density and driving behavior made me think about growth and development in Vermont. How many more jobs, homes, and, ultimately, people would be a good thing? Sure, when my kids grow up I'd like them to find employment locally so they can stay here, but at what price? Frankly, I'd rather they moved away to find jobs than have them stay in a Vermont that's become so crowded that people lose their connection to the community. It's not just driving habits that are affected by population. How big can a town become and still have a Town Meeting that works? How small must a town be for mom-and-pop stores to survive? And how low does the population have to stay for the land-scape to support farms and forests? Quality of life is clearly a subjective matter, but a lot of what I value about living in Vermont would not be possible if it were heavily populated. So while I'm all for economic opportunity, we should be careful about how we create it. After all, it's not so bad to slow down and enjoy the ride.

A (Metaphorical)
Garden Invasion

My neighbor's garden is always a mess.

Every year the weeds grow five feet tall, there are plant diseases of every type, and crops sprawl untended on the ground. Timely harvests get missed, so the produce is overripe and covered with blemishes by the time it's picked. The rogue gardener in command of this operation then torments his own family with hideous fruits and vegetables.

After the growing season is over, plants are left in the garden to rot on the ground all through the winter. Then, come spring, fungal pathogens sporulate with abandon and bacterial populations explode on every surface. These biological weapons are threats to the agricultural stability of the neighborhood.

I've asked him nicely to clean up his act. I've begged. I've threatened to report him to the Master Gardeners. What really gets my goat is that *I* got him started in this whole business by giving him some packets of seeds and a couple of gardening books many years ago.

Now he's left me no choice. I'm going to invade.

That's right—my antihorticultural assets are gathering at the border. I'm going in; I'm taking the dog, two kids with a soccer ball, and a rototiller will bring up the rear. We're going to destroy any and all gardening violations we encounter. It won't be pretty, but it's got to be done or the madness will continue. Raised beds will be felled, decaying vegetation will be composted, and walkways will be liberated of weeds. Order will be restored, as it should be in civilized society.

I thought of asking other neighbors if they'd like to help with my invasion, but frankly I don't care if they come along or not. I've got what it takes to get the job done, and I'm sure they'll appreciate my effort in the end, even if they won't admit it in public.

Of course, I haven't really figured out what will happen next year. I suppose the cycle of neglect could begin again. What if his children take over the garden, and they're even worse?

Perhaps I'll set up an inspection schedule to make sure that hoeing, picking, and spraying are performed according to Cooperative Extension standards. Maybe I'll take pictures to document infractions and keep a journal of violations. There's no doubt I'll be busy keeping an eye out for unacceptable behavior for years to come. And maybe that's good, because while I'm spending all this time minding my neighbor's business, I won't really have time to face up to the problems in my own yard, where the blueberries need mulching, the apples need pruning, and I never did get around to planting a cover crop.

Restraint Is the Key

It takes a brilliant speaker to cover a depressing topic and make you come away inspired. Bill McKibben, an environmental author, did just that as the keynote speaker for a conference called "Something Wild, Something Managed."

The conference was sponsored by the Middlebury College Environmental Studies program, in celebration of the program's thirty-fifth year and the college's 200th. The focus of the event was the role of wilderness in the Northeast, its value, and how wilderness can fit into the larger landscape.

McKibben presented a good-news, bad-news big picture of the environment, and our own landscape here in the Northeast is actually part of the good news. Although it's not always obvious to us, there's been a renewal of wildness in the Northeast. Terrain that was largely cleared a century ago has been reforested, wildlife that was once virtually eliminated has returned, including beaver, moose and fisher, and heavy industries that not long ago were polluting the soil and water have moved away or cleaned up their acts. This transformation speaks of redemption and offers hope based on the resilience of the planet to heal itself once people stop inflicting ecological wounds.

But the bad news is very bad indeed. For one thing, this kind of renewal is a rare occurrence on planet Earth. In fact, human beings are quite busily damaging natural systems around the world. Most alarming of all is the trend in global warming and its potential impact.

Ten years ago, McKibben wrote a book called *The End of Nature*, which was a wake-up call based on the theory that the Earth was getting hotter because greenhouse gases such as carbon dioxide were accumulating in the atmosphere. Now, a decade later, global warming is no longer a theory but a scientific fact, and the debate has turned from whether or not the planet is warming to how much it will warm over the next century. Among the dozens of predictive models that have been developed, the worst-case scenario is an increase of four degrees, and the best-case scenario is an increase of two degrees. Now that's depressing. But as McKibben pointed out, that difference of degrees is worth fighting for. Why? Because the more the Earth warms, the greater the change in weather patterns, sea levels, and ecosystems. We're already seeing record-high global temperatures, storms of greater intensity, and, here in the Northeast, a shortening of winter. The oceans are rising, too, not just because polar ice is melting, but because water expands as it gets warmer. There are plenty of jokes about the coming of oceanside property to Vermont, but in coastal cities and low-lying agricultural areas, like most of Florida or Bangladesh, the impacts of global warming will be catastrophic.

So what can we do? McKibben suggests we try some restraint. Not only does the United States lead the world in consumption, whether it's fossil fuels or fast food, but we also promote consuming as a way of life. It's hard to figure why the rest of the world wants to be like us, but they do. The catch, of course, is that the planet can't support the United States consuming what it does for much longer, let alone billions of others doing the same. So we need to change. We need to model a new-and-improved lifestyle, one that's more connected to nature, less devoted to material things, and ultimately more satisfying than the race to own ever-larger homes with ever-more-perfect lawns and ever-larger cars in the driveway for taking trips to ever-larger malls.

Since many of you have already wondered *Is that all there is?* it may be easier than we think to transform our notion of fulfillment. It won't happen fast, but even little steps in the direction of ecological sanity are better than none. Protecting wild places is one such step. After all, wilderness is the only place where there's lots of good stuff, but nothing to buy. We need wild places because they help us remember what's really important: life, nature, family, community, service. In other words, it's not just the economy, stupid.

Agriculture's Secret Weapon

A gricultural education isn't particularly touchy-feely—there's not a lot of hugging or handholding going on when farmers meet, and your typical extension meeting doesn't focus on expressing feelings or connecting to one's inner self. So when I stumbled upon the secret weapon of agricultural sustainability, I knew it was going to be a hard sell.

My discovery came during a tour of farms in southern New Jersey, but it could have been unearthed most anywhere if I'd been paying attention. Southern Jersey, contrary to popular belief, has rural land that abounds with agricultural production. This fact was obvious from the bus window as field after field rolled by.

Our first stop was a brand-new peach-packing house owned by a consortium of local farmers. These farmers have an unusual partner: a South American peach distributor who supplies fruit in the off season. This arrangement means that the New Jersey growers can pack and sell peaches on a year-round basis, which is essential to the facility's profitability. It wasn't easy for the farmers to join up with a former competitor, but it made sense to do so.

Next, we visited a vegetable farmer specializing in Asian greens. He relies on a single buyer that supplies mom-and-pop ethnic stores in New York City. That buyer helped him identify which varieties of these unusual crops were in demand, where to get the seed, and how to translate the instructions on the seed packages. Unlike other buyers, this fellow waits for his farmer's crops to come in rather than seeking them out elsewhere.

And he pays a fair price, and he pays on time. In exchange he gets a plentiful local supply of the products he needs.

At another farm, the owner described his Mexican labor crew to us. "They're not laborers," he said. "They're agricultural professionals!"

This farmer treats his workers exceptionally well, almost like family. He provides them with a nice apartment, full medical and dental benefits, and the ability to earn top wages based on performance. In return he gets top performance, along with experienced and reliable employees who return year after year. That gives him the freedom to focus his attention on other areas of management, and to even take a vacation once in a while.

These farms—and others like them that buck the standard arrangements for marketing products or managing labor—have something in common: committed relationships. Don't be alarmed; I'm not leading up to couples therapy. I'm talking about business partnerships, where employees, customers, and farmers are loyal to one another because a win-win situation has been established.

It's obvious that trusting relationships are critical to farms that want to develop new markets for their products, farms that want reliable labor, and farms that want loyal customers. But you won't find *relationships* listed as a topic on an extension program anytime soon. However, there will be a lot more discussion taking place about how to succeed with marketing agreements, provide excellent customer service, and improve employee relations. Because despite all the benefits of technology and the wonders of agricultural ecology, the human element of farming is far too important to ignore.

Assessing Biotechnology
in the Field

Most consumers in Vermont are less than enthusiastic about the use of biotechnology in food production. A survey of 697 registered voters, conducted by the Center for Rural Studies at the University of Vermont, found that 72 percent of Vermonters are concerned about genetically modified organisms, or GMOs, in food and agriculture, 67 percent believe that GMOs pose a risk to human health and the environment, and 60 percent do not have confidence that government agencies can effectively regulate GMOs. Vermonters support labeling of products that contain GMOs: Ninety-four percent said that processed foods containing GMOs should be labeled, and 95 percent said that genetically modified agricultural products should be labeled.

Even if we agree with regulators that GMO foods are safe to eat, there are other reasons to label them. One is to allow consumers to err on the side of caution; another is to allow consumers to choose what kind of farming they want to support with their food dollars. Scientists who have concerns about GMOs tend to be more worried about their impact on ecosystems and farming practices than they are about potential food-safety risks.

Genetically engineered or transgenic crops are particularly worrisome, because tens of millions of acres are already in this kind of production and are interacting directly with the environment. This sets these crops apart from GMOs in laboratories, medical facilities, or barns. For example, cows treated with recombinant bovine growth hormone won't transfer genetic information to wild relatives, but bioengineered, virus-resistant squash plants might do just that.

Transgenic crops also threaten ecologically sound farming practices such as the use of the bioinsecticide *Bacillus thuringiensis* or *B.t.,* which organic and ecological farms rely on to control caterpillars and potato beetles. The widespread planting of cotton, corn, and potato varieties that have been engineered to contain *B.t.* in their leaves are likely to promote development of pest populations that are resistant to *B.t.,* rendering it ineffective.

Organic farms are especially at risk from transgenic crops. Since GMOs are prohibited by organic farming standards, including the pending national standards, certified organic farmers and processors risk losing their markets if their products get contaminated with GMOs. That might occur by the movement of pollen from nearby fields of GMO crops, by the accidental sowing of transgenic crops on organic farms, or by mixing with GMO products during handling or processing.

And it's not just organic farmers who are concerned about transgenic crops. A conventional vegetable farmer told me that he was "horrified" that he might have planted transgenic vegetables without knowing it. That can happen because these vegetable varieties are usually described in seed catalogs as pest-resistant—a good thing—without mentioning that they're also transgenic. A conventional dairy farm family was upset when their seed supplier delivered transgenic corn after running out of the variety that had been ordered. No permission was asked, no contract presented, and no planting instructions provided.

Both organic and conventional farms deserve protection from the ecological and marketplace risks posed by GMOs. Not only is more research needed to identify and avoid those risks, but the informational playing field needs to be leveled, too. There's been a massive financial investment in agricultural biotechnology. To balance that, more funding is needed to study ecosystem-based agriculture that relies on practices like crop rotation, biological pest control, and habitat management. Sadly, because these studies won't result in many products that can be sold to farmers, they won't generate a lot of corporate support. But compared to biotechnology, this approach could be just as effective at enhancing farm profitability while posing fewer risks to the environment and doing a much better job of maintaining public confidence in the food system.

Community Supported
Agriculture

C ommunity supported agriculture, or CSA, is one of the bright spots in farming today. CSA is an arrangement where consumers purchase a share in a local farm's harvest prior to the growing season. In return, they get a weekly distribution of food, usually a box of fresh vegetables. Sometimes known as subscription farming, CSA farming is growing by leaps and bounds, and these CSAs represent an opportunity for people to get started in a challenging career as a grower. A CSA farm can start small, with relatively low overhead, so for many young farmers they're just the ticket. Maybe that's why the CSA conferences I've attended have been full of people in their 20s and 30s, something that's pretty unusual at agricultural meetings.

It was only a decade ago that CSA farms started to spring up in this country. Now, in 2000, there are over 1,000 of them, including thirty in Vermont. The largest ones have several hundred families as shareholders, like the Intervale Community Farm in Burlington; the smallest ones are usually neighborhood based, where only a handful of families get food from a farm just down the road. On average, though, the typical CSA farm in the Northeast serves fifty to a hundred families, each paying anywhere from $250 to $500 a year. The price of a share depends on how much and what type of products are provided, and for how long. Most CSA shares are for three or four months of vegetables, but some shares include cut flowers, herbs, or berries, and some include winter shares of storage vegetables. There are also CSA operations that distribute eggs, meats, and value-added products like bread, jam, or salsa. At Bingham Brook Farm in Charlotte, you can even get farm-baked pizza.

CSA shareholders share the risks of crop production with farmer, which isn't something that everybody is comfortable with. However, the risk is pretty low, because even in a tough growing season, when many crops yield less than expected, others do just fine. In addition, most CSAs are run by farmers who know how to manage risk; they plan for adversity with diversity by growing many different kinds of crops and by making multiple plantings of each one.

Studies have shown that CSA farms provide more value to the consumer than either conventional or organic supermarkets. Plain and simple, shareholders get more food for their dollar. Not only that, they get the very freshest food with the least possible packaging. Joining a CSA farm also helps keep your food dollars within the community, because all the money goes directly to the farmer. But what I like best about CSA membership is the farm experience. Once a week you get to visit your farm, and you can hang out for a while if you want to. The kids get to run around, check out the farm animals, see where their food comes from, and help with the pick-your-own crops like flowers, peas, and strawberries.

More and more farmers are discovering CSA as an alternative market. Because CSA eliminates a lot of packaging and distribution costs, it helps farms be more profitable. CSA also reduces the need to meet the conventional market demand for perfect and uniform appearance, so the farmer can use those crooked carrots or those potatoes with a blemish or two instead of throwing them away.

Belonging to a CSA farm isn't for everyone. It's not as convenient or as flexible as going to the supermarket. You'll also have to make some adjustments to your eating habits by trying some vegetables that you haven't tried before, and by eating a bit more seasonally, based on what's being harvested at the farm. But for consumers who want to eat the freshest food, contribute to farm profitability, and have a chance to connect with local agriculture, they offer a great opportunity.

Weed Wars

There's a bucket of toxic waste in waste in my car. It isn't poisonous in the usual sense of the word, but it contains the horticultural equivalent of plutonium. You see, it's a bucket of soil, and that soil is loaded with *weed seeds*.

Oh, I know, weeds are nature's way of keeping Earth's tender surface protected from nakedness; they are also indicators of soil fertility. Weeds recycle nutrients in the soil and provide habitat for beneficial insects. On the other hand, you can't eat them, you can't sell them, and they'll take over a field if you let them. So to many farmers and gardeners, weeds are enemy number one, and a lot of effort goes into weed control.

In agriculture, herbicides account for the vast majority of pesticide use in terms of the total amount applied. But on some farms, weeds are managed mostly with nonchemical controls. For example, mulches such as straw or black plastic are used to suppress weeds, and cover crops like buckwheat or sorghum-sudangrass are grown to hold summertime weeds in check when a field is being rested from crop production. And to kill the weeds that inevitably grow among the crop rows, there are cultivators of all kinds, designed to dig up, cut up, bury, or burn weeds without damaging the crop. Rototillers may be a popular tool for gardeners, but farmers have many more tools in their weed-control arsenal. There are rolling cultivators, basket weeders, finger weeders, spider weeders, and tine weeders. And increasingly common on organic vegetable farms are flame weeders for killing small weeds with a short dose of high heat, which is great fun for pyromaniacs.

Of course prevention is the preferred method of weed management, since cultivation takes time and money. Preventing weeds means composting manure to kill the seeds, mowing or plowing weeds before they make new seeds, and avoiding the importation of weeds with purchased plants or soil amendments.

The bucket in my car represents an ounce of weed prevention, although I almost opted for a pound of cure. You see, it started when I dug up some perennials from a field near my office. I know the field well, and it's a weedy one, but the offer of free delphiniums and columbines was too tempting to resist, so I brought some plants home. To minimize the stress of transplanting, I dug up a big ball of soil with each plant. At the time, there weren't many weeds to be seen since it was early in the growing season. The few quackgrass rhizomes I encountered were removed with great care, as if they were dangerous parasites. Left intact, these fleshy underground stems of what's locally known as witchgrass would proliferate, and soon my flowers would be fighting for breathing space. If you've battled witchgrass before, you know: The more you hoe it and the more you till it, the more you spread it. A witch's potion indeed!

But the real black magic in these clumps of soil was hidden from view— seeds of annual weeds like Johnsongrass and large crabgrass, plus nasty broadleaves like redroot pigweed and lambsquarters. These tall-growing weeds start out small, but, left unchecked, they explode in size and release thousands of seeds per plant. Worst of all is hairy galinsoga, or quickweed. It flowers before you can say *boo*, and sets viable seeds inside flowers that look like they just opened. I was just about to set out my free plants in their new home when I had a premonition: I saw myself bent over, pulling, plucking, hacking, and whacking, cursing the soil I'd brought home with these plants. In a panic, I started shaking root balls over a bucket. So much for careful transplanting—those perennials went in bare-rooted, shaken half to death, and with barely a particle of soil on them.

So now I'm stuck with a pail of soil containing thousands of nature's noxious warheads. In a moment of temporary insanity, I considered unilateral disarmament by dumping the soil on my compost pile. Instead, I've decided on repatriation. I'm gonna dump that soil back in the field where it came from—as soon as I get a hazardous waste disposal permit.

Bug Camp

I magine you're seven years old, and that bugs are your life. Okay, you've dabbled in Pokeman, and reptiles hold a certain allure, but basically you're an entomologist at heart. Creeping, crawling, flying, or at rest, insects are for you the best. Your enthusiasm for arthropods knows no bounds, and it's rubbed off on classmates and friends alike. In kindergarten, you've left a legacy of bug love, in that all the kids now know about larvae, pupae, and other insect life stages. Instead of squealing with disgust, they now delight in their encounters with caterpillars, beetles, and the like. Even your parents have come to view the insect world with renewed respect, and they've adjusted to living with news flashes on local bug behavior that are issued pretty much from sunup to sundown.

So what's the highlight of your summer vacation? Why it's bug camp, of course! And there really *is* a bug camp—it takes place in Brattleboro, Vermont at the Bonneyvale Environmental Education Center, or BEEC. For one week each summer, six-to-eight-year-olds learn all about insects, including their habitats, how they communicate, and how they sense the world. They glorify bugs with bug-based stories, bug games, and of course, bug art. And what would bug camp be without bug songs? After a full week of this, you would think even the most dedicated junior entomologists have had just about enough.

But not the one I happen to live with. No, for him there is no limit to bug-based activities. Maybe that explains the caterpillar frass on our kitchen table, the crickets in the bedroom, and why my wife and I spend our spare time building bug boxes and rearing organisms that other parents are squishing. We thought that bug camp would give us a break, but instead it took our entomological conversations to levels we hadn't dreamed of, like bug morality and insect justice. You see, bug camp isn't all fun and games. Once you look closely, it's clear that the bug world is full of complex life-and-death issues. Take the tomato hornworm, for example.

Gardeners are familiar with this large and voracious caterpillar that can defoliate tomato plants in a jiffy, and it's also pretty common to find these caterpillars covered with tiny white cocoons. These cocoons contain the immature form of a parasitic wasp that lays its eggs in the caterpillar, where they hatch and then feed on the host as they develop. So when the kids find a parasitized hornworm in the garden, there are things they want to know: *Does it hurt? Is it right? What should we do with it?* And although the general answer is that it's all a part of the cycle of nature, it's a tough pill to swallow for little bug lovers.

Bug camp is just one of a half a dozen summer-camp sessions offered by BEEC, which is a non-profit organization founded in the early '90s. Its mission is to provide people in the community with opportunities to explore and learn about their natural environment. BEEC's 100-acre farm in West Brattleboro, Vermont, provides a perfect setting for summer camps with themes about animals, wilderness survival skills, nature discovery, and storytelling. The old farm buildings are surrounded by rolling hills filled with meadows, woods, and ponds, all of which, of course, contain insects.

In addition to the summer camps, BEEC provides educational programs to kids through collaborations with local schools, Big Brothers and Big Sisters, and SWEEP, Vermont's Statewide Environmental Education Program. Over 2,000 children participated in BEEC's school programs and Sunday-morning nature walks last year, and local communities were served by BEEC's ongoing monitoring of water quality in rivers and streams. BEEC also sponsors special programs; my own favorite is the annual visit of Veedor the Condor. It's pretty exciting when a bird with a ten-foot wingspan does a fly-by just over your head. Well, maybe not as exciting as finding an iridescent green dung beetle, especially a male with that horn on its head, a discovery that leads to more questions: "Hey Dad, can we keep it, just for a while? I promise I'll let it go. And can we can get some dung? And another bug box?"

Ladybugs: The Good, the Bad, and the Spotted

Ladybugs, lady beetles, or ladybird beetles are probably the best-known predatory insects. There are over 450 different species in North America, some of them native and some introduced. The majority of these bugs are beneficial because they feed on aphids and other insect pests. But you can have too much of a good thing—if you've ever experienced an invasion of ladybugs, you know what I mean. Around the time of Halloween, hundreds, sometimes thousands of ladybugs descend on people's homes, looking for a place to spend the winter. They come in through cracks, windows, and doorways. After crawling about on ceilings and walls for a few weeks, they find a nook or a cranny and settle in for a long nap. In the spring they reappear, looking for a way out.

This onslaught of uninvited guests is a relatively new occurrence in Vermont. While other species of ladybugs prefer to overwinter outdoors under a comfy blanket of leaves, bark, and decaying organic matter, one species in particular has taken a hankering to cohabitating with humans. This is the Asian ladybug, or Halloween ladybug. It's a new arrival to the continent, introduced by the U.S. Department of Agriculture to the deep South a couple of decades ago, where it was supposed to prey on the insect pests of southern trees like pecans. It apparently had its own plan in mind, since the Asian ladybug has since moved northward, adapting to the cold winters by using buildings as overwintering sites.

Asian ladybugs are not harmful, but human reaction to them might be. While under siege, some homeowners will call up Cooperative Extension offices asking what pesticides can be sprayed in their bedrooms. I suggest less toxic control methods instead, and explain that a vacuum cleaner is pretty safe. Sucking up the bugs on a daily basis for a week or two will keep the invasion down to a dull roar. Kind-hearted souls who don't want to kill the ladybugs should put in a new bag each time they vacuum, then empty the bugs outside. I, for one, put them in my greenhouse. After all, this ladybug is a valuable pest-control tool, and if you don't have a house-ful of them and actually want to buy some from a beneficial bug supplier, they're pretty expensive. As the fall days get cooler and shorter, though, you just might have a neighbor with a few thousand extra who will give you a very good deal.

Another species, the convergent lady beetle, is not expensive to buy commercially, and is probably more effective for biological pest control in the garden or greenhouse than the Asian ladybug, which prefers to seek out pests in trees. But like the Asian ladybug, the convergent lady beetle is also not a native Vermonter. This insect is collected from hibernation sites in the foothills of the Sierra Nevada mountains in California, and it has to be preconditioned on a special diet before being sold. Otherwise, it would migrate away once it was released, as it would have done after hibernating back in its native environment. Hibernation is good for the appetite; a convergent lady beetle can eat up to fifty aphids per day.

The superstar of beneficial lady beetles in the Northeast is the pink-spotted ladybug. This beetle is a native, and quite common in the garden. It's more oval in shape than other ladybugs, and pinker, too. Hardly a fussy eater, it consumes a variety of pests, including aphids, mites, and the eggs of corn borer, corn earworm, potato beetle, imported cabbageworm, and asparagus beetle. Both the larvae and the adults are predaceous.

Next spring, look closely in the garden; you'll probably notice several other lady beetle species. For example, the seven-spotted lady beetle was introduced from Europe for control of aphids. Rather a glutton, it can eat several hundred aphids a day, which may have to do with its relatively large size. It's a third of an inch long, with a distinctive domed shape and white spots on either side of its head. The nine-spotted lady beetle is the official insect of New York. It doesn't always have nine spots, but it does eat asparagus beetles and their eggs, as well as aphids. Easiest of all the lady beetles to identify is the red lady beetle—less than a quarter of an inch long and a pale orange-red, it looks quite different from the nine-spotted and seven-spotted species, mostly because it has no spots at all.

Measuring Agricultural Production

L ies, damn lies, and statistics. So said someone famous, maybe the first presidential pollster. And to some extent it's true that statistics sometimes distort the facts—did you hear the one about the statistician that looked at the data and concluded the average person has one breast and one testicle?

In any event, there are groups of people that dwell on statistics, and one such organization is the New England Agricultural Statistics Service. Every year they collect and analyze all kinds of data about farming in the Northeast, and the numbers they generate are very helpful to understanding what's going on with agriculture here.

An analysis of the sales of farm products in 1999 shows that Vermont was tops in New England: Our farmers took in $542 million, or just over a quarter of the $2.1 billion in farm cash receipts that were generated by the six states. Maine and Connecticut weren't far behind in total agricultural sales, but they sold a very different mix of products.

In Vermont, milk was far and away the largest source of farm cash receipts, accounting for more than three-quarters of total sales. In Maine, the most diversified state in the region, milk accounted for just under a quarter of cash receipts, about the same as potatoes. Connecticut is dominated by the greenhouse and nursery industry, which contributed over a third of its ag sales, more than twice the value of milk in that state.

New England-wide, milk is still number one. At three-quarters of a billion dollars, it accounts for a third of all farm cash receipts. Greenhouse and nursery products are number two, at $422 million. Vegetables, including Maine's potatoes, are a distant third at $250 million.

Sales of crops go up and down over the years, and sometimes it's a roller-coaster ride. Changes in the overall value of a particular commodity are a function of the prices farmers receive, or the yields they harvest, or both. For example, the value of milk went down 2 percent from 1998 to 1999, despite increased production, because the price paid to farmers fell by an average of 52 cents per hundredweight. Cash sales of cranberries during the same one-year period dropped by 25 percent, and by a whopping 72 percent over two years, as prices paid to farmers declined dramatically. When the value of a commodity drops, despite stable or rising prices, that's usually a reflection of difficult growing conditions. In 1999, one of the hottest and driest summers on record, sales of dry hay were down by 21 percent. Vegetable yields suffered too, but sales dropped only by 3 percent, in part because most vegetable growers used irrigation to cope with the lack of rainfall.

Farm cash receipts provide a pretty good snapshot of what's being sold by farms, but the numbers reflect only a small portion of the agricultural economy. This is because the cash receipts are based only on the income farmers get from sales of raw products and does not include the value that is added to these products, either on or off the farm, when they are processed into cheese, yogurt, cider, or a whole host of other products. Farm cash receipts also don't reflect the economic contribution of diversified farms that harvest timber, produce lumber, resell products from other farms, or accommodate tourists. When you add in those numbers, the economic impact of agriculture to the region becomes enormous.

But the value of agriculture is not just economic. Farming's contribution to the region's appearance, culture, wildlife, and quality of life is something that statisticians will never be able to put an accurate number on. But it sure would be nice if they tried.

Grants for Farmers

I f you are a public servant with an educational mission, whether you work for Cooperative Extension or another agency, and if you want to start a new and exciting project, you probably don't have the money for it just lying around. So you take the idea, bounce it around in your brain for a while, let it filter down through your fingertips to a keyboard, and then *voila*, it bursts forth onto paper as—a grant proposal. If the idea is a good one, and if you've made a compelling case for it, and you're a little bit lucky, you might just get funded. If not, you've got to try again. These days, it's not just researchers that have to write grants to pay for what they do. There's a parade of educators and advocates with dreams in their minds and dollar signs in their eyes that are lining up to seek grants from government agencies and private foundations.

Many people I work with are looking for money to do things that will help agriculture. Of course, along the way we'll help ourselves, too, by paying for salaries, fringe benefits, travel, and office expenses. Helping agriculture can get pretty expensive, and sometimes I think it's too bad we can't just give the money directly to farmers.

It turns out that there is a grant program that does just that. The Northeast Sustainable Agriculture Research and Education program, or SARE, has a special grant program aimed at helping farmers who have a good idea and want to figure out if it works. The Farmer Grant program started in 1993, when thirty-six projects were funded. Last year, sixty-two farmers were awarded a total of $270,000. The average grant was $4,300.

Unlike other grant applications, the farmer grant forms are quite simple. No literature reviews, no abstracts, no requirement to submit twenty copies plus a file on diskette. Instead, it's just a few pages, using plain language and a straightforward budget. Farmers do have to clearly describe what they want to investigate and how they're going to go about it, and they do have to show what they'll use the money for—supplies, special equipment, or hired help, for example. Grants are made for up to $10,000, although many farmers ask for just a few hundred dollars to help them test their ideas. Applicants are urged to provide a match, by showing in the budget the value of what they will contribute, such as their time or the use of equipment.

Farmers are remarkably creative people and the grants awarded to date sure prove that. For example, a farmer in Vermont looked at using chickens to control Colorado potato beetles, and another worked to develop new markets for goat and lamb meat. In Massachusetts, someone tried using dogs to keep birds out of blueberries, and someone else tried growing strawberries in a greenhouse. In Maryland, a farmer looked at improving the nutrition of grazing dairy cows by supplementing their diet with molasses, while in West Virginia, ginseng production under pawpaw trees was examined. In New Hampshire, a solar vehicle was developed for farm use.

Farmers have also gotten funds to provide training to other farmers and to the public. There was an educational project on farmstead cheese-making in Connecticut; a Vermont farmer taught people about the use of woodland plants and wildflowers in the home garden; in Pennsylvania, a farmer developed 4-H workshops on sustainable approaches to raising beef.

The farmers receiving these grants are not expected to do replicated scientific research. They are expected to have clear goals, a good plan, and to document what happens. It's also important for the farmers to partner with extension or another agency that will help them with troubleshooting during the project and with publicizing the results.

As one farmer told me, "These SARE grants are something special. They are a great opportunity for farmers, and, unlike so many other programs, this one is really aimed at helping the little guy solve problems."

Environmental Learning
for the Future

Public speaking is something that most people would prefer to avoid. For those of us who have to do it, it helps to harness the fear it engenders and use that adrenaline for the entertainment of the audience. But sometimes it's tough to just hold people's attention, let alone entertain them.

The worst is when your audience starts to nod off. That's happened to me more than once when addressing farmers at nighttime meetings; awake since the wee hours of the morning and faced with less-than-riveting information, their eyelids fall even as the volume of my voice rises. But lately I've been talking to an audience with boundless energy, one that's busting at the seams to interject comments, whose bodies literally squirm with excitement about new concepts, and where the honesty is brutal; if my words aren't clear, brows furrow in unison and shoulders sag with disappointment. I'm talking about first graders.

Every month I visit the local school as an ELF volunteer—ELF stands for Environmental Learning for the Future, a program initiated by the Vermont Institute of Natural Science almost thirty years ago. It has a simple mission: to connect children with the natural world. ELF's strategy is also simple: to train parents and other volunteers to teach nature education to children in their local elementary schools. This year, more than 1,300 volunteers and seventy-five Vermont schools are participating in ELF.

The program is fun and easy to do. It's based on a collection of classroom and outdoor activities that the volunteers use to help the kids understand the environment. These activities have been collected into a book called *Hands-On Nature*, which I highly recommend to anyone who wants to explore nature with children. The book has five sections: habitats, adaptations, cycles, earth and sky, and designs of nature. In the Dummerston school where I volunteer, one of these sections is presented each year, from kindergarten through fourth grade. There are two or three volunteers for each class, and all the classes work with the same section in a given year. That way, all the volunteers can prepare together for going into the classroom.

Every month, the ten of us meet in the basement of the local church, where we do a dry run of that month's activities. One volunteer acts as the presenter and the rest of us play the role of the kids. Each set of activities starts with a puppet show that introduces key concepts and interactions. Then the class engages in a mixture of indoor and outdoor investigation, large-group sharing, and small-group observation.

This year we're learning about habitats. *What's a habitat?* It's the community in which an animal lives. *What are four things that a habitat must provide?* Food, water, shelter, and a place to raise young. So far this fall, we've checked out some very different kinds of habitats, including a field, a forest floor, and rotting logs. We have found out that different animals live in different habitats, and we have looked up close and personal at critters like earthworms and bark beetles, who are very particular about where they live. We even used a time machine to see how a log changes as it slowly rots over several years. Along the way we learned that composers write music, but decomposers break down leaves and wood into small pieces.

Going into the classroom as a volunteer has given me a renewed respect for people who do the real teaching, day in and day out. Education is hard work. Besides the subject matter preparation, it takes a lot of energy to keep the kids focused and to help them with their social skills. A couple of hours with twenty-one seven-year-olds makes you realize just how run down your batteries really are, and what the fine art of digression is all about. But what a joy it is to watch children as their minds grasp new ideas, as they take pleasure in the world around them, and as they delight in the interconnectedness of nature.

2001

The Future: A Newscast

The year is 2051, and this is all things that *might* be considered, brought to you by NPR-NBC-CNN. President Ralph Nader, Jr. traveled to Europe today in an effort to revive stalled trade negotiations. The Europeans want to ban all American imports in a last-ditch effort to salvage the remnants of their cultural heritage; the President is expected to offer funding for cultural museums and to propose limiting exports of fast food and B movies.

The state of California and Archer Daniels-Dow Chemical agreed to merge today, creating the largest public-private hybrid corporation ever formed under a new law that allows for the combining of commercial and government entities. The new state corporation will be called CaliDownia, Inc. A prepared statement declared this to be a victory for all citizens, because the new partnership will bypass the bureaucratic oversight that hampers the productivity of our food-and-fiber system. The costs of lobbying lawmakers and conforming to state regulations will now be avoided, leading to significant savings that can be passed on to consumers.

The U.S. Department of Agribusiness today approved the commercial production of genetically engineered milk. A spokesrecording for the department said that the milk, produced by specialized microorganisms, has been thoroughly tested and is absolutely safe for human consumption. It's estimated that the new milk-producing technology will save dairy farmers hundreds of billions of dollars annually by avoiding the need to have cows. The Food, Drug, and Recreational Supplements Administration has ruled that genetically engineered milk is substantially equivalent to regular milk, and therefore will not require any special labeling to distinguish it from milk that comes from outmoded animals.

In other agribusiness news, the deconstruction of shopping malls in the Midwest continues. Missouri and Iowa, now largely covered by parking lots, highways, and retail outlets, have embarked on an ambitious program to reclaim their once-great farming resource: soil. A multitrillion-dollar fund has been established for the purchase of demolition rights at malls located on prime agricultural land. These malls are purchased at their agricultural use value, knocked down, and the debris trucked to the Grand Canyon National Landfill. The former mall sites are then made available to qualified farmers from Mexico, Cuba, and Brazil under the Farmer Immigration Act, designed to supplement the dangerously low number of remaining American farmers.

A strike by workers at Microsoft-AOL-Time-AT&T-Sony threatens to bring national electronic interfacing to a standstill. Monthly updates of office software, as required by law, are not taking place, and within the year many companies across the nation will have hopelessly obsolete communication networks. In an emergency measure, the Secretary of Communication Services has called for a temporary reactivation of the telephone system.

In local news, Vermont ski areas petitioned the Agency of Natural and Synthetic Resources for permission to cover an additional ten square miles of slopes with Teflon. Global warming has led to the conversion of all ski areas to grassboarding, and it's become increasingly difficult to maintain live grass surfaces without natural rainfall. The Teflon coating not only avoids the need for water but offers a faster ride without causing grass stains after a fall. However, the impact of Teflon on wildlife is a slippery subject that may require further study.

In the legislature, Act 6000 continues to stir debate. The proposed legislation provides for statewide education funding based on a formula that calculates a town's annual expenditure on prescription drugs, divided by the number of civil unions it has performed, times the average annual sales of maple syrup. Opponents say that the law encourages the consumption of sweets.

From NPR-NBC-CNN, in the year 2051, this has been all things that *might* be considered.

A Systems Approach to
Agricultural Research

Natural systems are remarkably powerful. That power comes from an incredibly complex web of interactions among a vast number of organisms and processes that are balanced, interconnected, and resilient. And although we believe, through the wonders of science, that we know a lot about the natural world, much of how it works remains a mystery.

Yet what is not known is rarely considered as ecosystems are manipulated left and right. The result of this interference is painfully obvious on a global scale, especially with regard to human management of water, soil, and food production. In all these areas, the focus has been on short-term goals, not on long-term sustainability.

The problems faced by agriculture are part and parcel of other ecological problems that have, at their root, the human desire to control and exploit. The path to sustainability for farming, and for human society, may well begin with greater humility, a more open mind, and a shift from domination of nature to collaboration with her.

Some agricultural scientists and farmers are waking up to this idea, but it isn't easy. On the one hand, farms are disturbed ecosystems, based on the manipulation of nature. To grow food, crops must be fed and pests must be controlled. But the consequences of intensive tillage, fertilization, and pesticide use are often unacceptable. On the other hand, new insights are emerging into how we might use the inherent strengths of farm ecosystems to accomplish our food-production goals.

For example, research shows that crop plants, when attacked by leaf-eating insects, actually send out a chemical call to beneficial insects, and these insects respond to that call by preying on the pests. This fantastic system is at work right under our noses, but we've been using pest-control methods that not only ignore, but sometimes suppress, its potential.

We're also failing to capitalize on evidence that healthy soil grows healthy plants, which in turn need fewer fertilizers and fungicides to be productive. This well-worn axiom of organic farming is increasingly being proven true by science. Practices like crop rotation and green manuring are now known to enhance the effects of beneficial soil microbes on plants. But economic pressures have driven farmers and researchers away from these time-tested techniques; instead of seeking stable-but-moderate levels of production with a minimum of off-farm inputs, the goal has been to develop farming systems with the highest possible production. This happens in spite of the farm's dependence on purchased inputs, and in spite of the negative economic consequences for many farmers.

But a new day is dawning. Not long ago, a group of progressive researchers, extension agents, farmers, and administrators from across the Northeast gathered to promote a systems approach to pest management. That's not as simple as studying a few new pest control techniques. Instead, it's as complicated as trying to figure out scientific methods that consider many interactions at once, and acknowledging the presence of effects that we don't even know how to measure, let alone statistically analyze. The barriers to adopting a systems approach aren't just scientific. They include professional challenges faced by researchers when they ask questions that don't readily lead to publications, won't get them promoted, and aren't often funded by government agencies. And the fact that farmers don't get rewarded in the marketplace for adopting practices aimed at long-term stewardship is another big obstacle.

But the consensus is that we *could* manage agricultural pests in an ecologically sound manner. By designing diversity into farming systems, optimizing soil health, and using inputs that don't poison natural processes, agriculture can lead the way for society as a whole in becoming more sustainable. The greater the support from consumers, academia, and public policy makers, the sooner this vision can be realized.

National Organic Standards

Over ten years in the making, based on dozens of public hearings, hundreds of committee meetings, and comments from 300,000 people, the United States Department of Agriculture presents . . . National Organic Standards.

The recently released organic rule brings to an end a decade-long debate over the definition of organic farming. The rule is a detailed description of the production practices, agricultural materials, processing methods, labeling requirements, and certification procedures that will legally qualify as organic. Now, the process of implementation begins. By September of 2002, the Organic Foods Production Act, originally passed by Congress in 1990, will be fully operational. That means that all organic farmers and food handlers must be in compliance; between now and then, the USDA will be hard at work accrediting many agencies, such as NOFA-Vermont, that will do the actual work of certifying organic farms.

Only accredited agencies will be allowed to grant certification to the 13,000 or so organic farms operating in the U.S. At this time, only half those farms are actually certified. The new standards will require the other half to either get with the program or stop selling their products as organic. Selling or labeling uncertified food as organic can result in a civil penalty of $10,000. Small farms that sell less than $5,000 worth of organic food each year won't have to get certified, although they will have to voluntarily adhere to the federal standards.

There are 1,100 certified organic farms in the Northeast; Pennsylvania, Maine, and Vermont each have more than 200. These farms will probably continue to be certified by their local certification agencies, assuming the agencies apply for and receive federal accreditation.

While there's something to be said for consistent organic standards, it's ironic that the success of organic farming as a grass-roots movement has culminated in national standards that effectively take away local control. And it's also ironic that organic farmers, who go the extra stewardship mile and incur the extra costs that result, have to pay for certification in order to get marketplace recognition.

In terms of production practices, the national standards are pretty strict. They require organic farms to use crop rotation and preventive pest management. Organic livestock must be raised entirely on organic feed, with access to the outdoors, and without growth-promoting hormones. The use of genetic engineering, sewage sludge, or irradiation in the production of organic food is prohibited. The standards go overboard in protecting food safety. Raw manure cannot be applied to any organic crop less than three months before harvest unless the manure has been composted at very high temperatures.

Although the final organic standards are vastly improved from earlier drafts, they remain an elaborate set of dos and don'ts designed to benefit interstate commerce by promoting consistency in organic farming; organic farmers themselves don't get a lot of benefit from them. Funding for organic research remains almost nonexistent, as does financial assistance for farmers making the transition to organic. And organic farms are still vulnerable to contamination from genetically modified organisms used by other farmers.

As the big players get into organic, it's like conventional-farming deja vu all over again. Small, local producers face competition from large, distant farms. Distributors seek out efficiency rather than quality, and corporations look to dominate the marketplace. What we really need is a national food policy that encourages local production, rural vitality, and long-term stewardship. Otherwise, the national organic standards will simply assure that, down the road, the corporate, mass-produced organic food we get from far away is almost as good as the local organic food we're used to now.

The Food Quality
Protection Act

There are four little letters that have many fruit and vegetable growers across the country in a cold sweat, while many environmentalists see the same four letters as a golden opportunity. Those letters are FQPA, and they stand for the Food Quality Protection Act.

The FQPA is a complex law that has dramatically changed the way the government regulates pesticides. After more than a decade of debate about pesticide policy, FQPA was unanimously approved by Congress in 1996. At the time, farmers and agricultural chemical companies endorsed the law because it changed the safety standard for pesticide residues on food from an impossible-to-achieve "zero-risk" to the more realistic standard of "a reasonable certainty of no harm." Environmentalists and public-health advocates supported FQPA because it required a safety review of all pesticides currently in use, and because it specifically attempted to protect children from pesticide risks.

Now, with the implementation of FQPA underway, farmers are worried that the law will threaten their livelihood by taking away the chemicals they need to control pests, while environmentalists are concerned that the law is not being enforced fast enough.

It takes a big spoonful of alphabet soup to understand what FQPA is all about. It all started with FIFRA, the Federal Insecticide, Fungicide and Rodenticide Act, introduced by Vermont's own Senator George Aiken in the late 1940s. Since then, several federal agencies have become involved in pesticide regulation. There's the USDA, the United States Department of

Agriculture, which collects data on what kind of pesticides are used on farms and how much. Along with the FDA—the Food and Drug Administration—the USDA also tests food for pesticide residues, and then provides that information to the EPA, the Environmental Protection Agency. The EPA decides which pesticides get registered for use and prescribes pesticide labeling and other regulations to protect people's health and the environment. The EPA also conducts dietary risk assessments and then sets the residue limits for pesticides on foods, which are called "tolerances."

The FQPA has dramatically changed the way the EPA sets the tolerances for pesticides on foods. No longer can the benefits of pesticide use be weighed against the risks. And in setting tolerances, the EPA is now required to pay special attention to children's sensitivity and exposure to pesticides, in part by including a safety factor of up to tenfold to account for uncertainty in the data it uses to determine risk. The EPA must also now consider *all* routes of pesticide exposure, such as drinking water and residential exposure, in addition to residues on food, when setting pesticide tolerances. That makes sense, because in some cases homeowner use of a pesticide may pose a more direct threat to the health of kids than agricultural uses do.

FQPA requires EPA to review all pesticide tolerances by 2006, so they've got their work cut out for them. There are more than 500 pesticide ingredients registered for use on food crops, and there are about 9,000 individual tolerances, each defining the permitted level of one residue on one food. EPA was required to start its review with the riskiest pesticides, mostly older chemicals, to make sure they meet current safety standards. At the same time, registrations of new, low-risk pesticides are supposed to be fast-tracked to help them reach the market quickly.

Now that EPA is about a third of the way through their work, a battle is shaping up. On one side are groups like the Natural Resources Defense Council, which cut a deal with EPA to settle a lawsuit aimed at speeding up the review of pesticides. No fair, claimed the American Crop Protection Association, which was not invited to help set the new, faster timetable. This group of ag chemical producers has some interesting allies, including animal rights groups, which oppose the testing of pesticides on laboratory animals. A federal judge will have to sort it all out but, either way, EPA will feel pressure from all sides as it continues its review of pesticides.

To quote the USDA, "Although the U.S. food supply is one of the safest in the world, public concern still exists about the effects of agricultural pesticides on human health and environmental quality." FQPA is a big step toward addressing that concern, but the EPA still has a long way to go to finish the job. Meanwhile, many agricultural groups are telling them to go slow, and many environmentalists are saying hurry up.

Donella Meadows

Thinking globally and acting locally makes a lot of sense. Most of us just don't have the energy to try and change the whole world, so we limit ourselves to doing what's possible—making a difference in our own communities. But a few exceptional people can do both, and one of those people was Donella Meadows. With her recent passing, both the planet and the Upper Valley* community have suffered a great loss.

Donella Meadows devoted her life to environmental sustainability, and her name has become synonymous with that concept. Her global and local efforts to promote a saner relationship with the Earth were remarkable. Trained as a biophysicist at Harvard, nearly thirty years ago she came to Dartmouth College, where she taught until her death in February.

In her writings, Donella explored not only the workings of environmental systems, but also the relationship that people have with those systems. She was a global educator, working on many books, including The Limits to Growth, which sold millions of copies in dozens of languages. She was persistent in her message, and twenty years after the book first appeared she helped update it, calling the new material Beyond the Limits.

Donella had many academic accomplishments, but she also reached out to everyday people. Her award-winning weekly column, "The Global

---

*The Upper Valley is a cultural region along the Connecticut River that includes portions of Vermont and New Hampshire. The unofficial capital of this region is Hanover, New Hampshire, home of Dartmouth College. —Ed.

Citizen," helped raise environmental awareness nationwide, appearing in more than twenty newspapers. Meadows also worked with public television producers to develop the ten-part series "Race to Save the Planet." She served on boards and committees all over the world, contributing to a variety of efforts aimed at enhancing our scientific understanding of environmental systems. Her efforts won her several prestigious fellowships.

On the local level Donella Meadows was also very active. She served on the board of the Trust for New Hampshire Lands, and she was a co-founder of the Upper Valley Land Trust. For twenty-seven years she lived on a small, communal, organic farm in Plainfield, New Hampshire, where she worked at sustainable resource management in a real and practical fashion. In 1999, she moved to Cobb Hill in Hartland Four Corners, Vermont. There she worked with others to establish a cohousing eco-village that offers a model of energy efficient design and land development that is in harmony with agriculture. The project includes housing that's clustered up on a hillside, saving the fertile bottomland for a diversified organic farm, a cheese-making facility, a community-supported agriculture program, and community gardens.

She was known to her friends as Dana, and while her words had great influence on me, I met her just once. I can only imagine how she affected the lives of those who worked closely with her. One of those people is Jim Schley, a poet and editor at Chelsea Green Press in White River Junction. Years ago, Jim was a student of Dana's. Soon after her death, he wrote, "No one has had more influence on the choices I've made in my life, the work that I do, the place that I live, and the way that I live. I feel more grateful than I can say for the luck of knowing her. Dana has suffered terribly in recent years while struggling with the accumulating proof that we are entering a new phase of danger. More so than most of us can bear, she has been one of those rare people who has confronted, with scientific agility and emotional candor, the true dimensions of the global ecological condition. We are now facing some of the greatest challenges ever experienced by life on this planet. My resolve, in her name, is to rededicate myself wholeheartedly to the process of opening hearts and minds to what hope remains."

Donella Meadows was an exceptional woman—in her mother's words, she was an "Earth missionary"—and she leaves an exceptional legacy of people she touched, and people who will carry on her work.

Colorado Potato Beetles

Anyone who grows potatoes is familiar with the Colorado potato beetle. This insect pest is one of the best-known beetles, famous for its ability to devour plants of the nightshade family, which includes potatoes, tomatoes, tobacco, eggplant, and peppers. The adult beetles and their voracious larvae can strip the plants of leaves and ruin an entire crop if left to their own devices.

The attractive, dome-shaped adults are nearly a half-inch long, yellow, with five black stripes on each wing cover. In late spring, after hibernating in the soil, usually along field edges, they emerge with one thing on their mind: a food source. They walk toward this goal for a few days until they build up the strength to fly toward it; everything about Colorado potato beetles involves a search for potato plants. Once they find them, the females start snacking and egg-laying, leaving clusters of bright yellow eggs on the undersides of the leaves. These eggs hatch into the soft-bodied, humpbacked larvae. They start out small but feed ravenously, molting four times as they grow to be quite plump. Then they crawl into the soil and pupate. From this resting stage, a second generation of adults emerges by the end of the season, ready to eat again before passing the winter underground.

What's amazing is that, not long ago, this pest was a harmless, well-behaved insect. It fed only on the buffalo burr, a tough weed that grows along the eastern foothills of the Rocky Mountains. Then the beetles suddenly discovered a new item on the menu in the white man's gardens. It adopted the cultivated potato as its favorite food, spread rapidly, and we've been fighting potato beetles ever since.

It happened like this: With the opening up of the West following the Mormon migration to Utah in 1847 and the California gold rush of 1849, pioneers arrived and planted potatoes. By 1855, potato growing reached westward to the native home of the beetle, and the insect started to spread eastward along the routes the pioneers traveled.

By hitchhiking and flying with the prevailing winds, it spread about eighty-five miles a year. It reached Nebraska in 1859, Illinois in 1864, Ohio in 1869, and the Atlantic coast in 1874. This caused great alarm overseas, and almost every European country banned the importation of American potatoes. That worked for a while: European potato-growing regions remained free of the pest until after World War I, when it appeared near Bordeaux, France, where there had been concentrations of American troops and supplies. Now the beetle is widespread in Europe, too.

Before our potato patches were invaded by the Colorado potato beetle, the name *potato bug* was applied to a long slender beetle with two black stripes on each wing cover. The adult of this beetle feeds on potatoes, but it lays its eggs in the ground and its predatory young feed on grasshopper eggs. Now a minor pest, it's called the *old-fashioned potato bug*.

There are many natural controls of Colorado potato beetle. Fungi infect them, beneficial insects attack them, and toads and birds eat them. Rarely, however, do these forces combine to offer sufficient control. So hand picking—followed by squishing, stomping, or drowning—is a popular defense among home gardeners.

Over the years, farmers have unleashed an arsenal of insecticides against the Colorado potato beetle, only to find it has developed resistance to many of them. Recently, some farmers have started laying traps for them in the form of plastic-lined trenches around their fields. Since the beetles can't fly when they first emerge, and they can't help but walk toward their favorite food, they fall into these shallow trenches. Once in there, they can't get out, and as the black plastic gets hot the beetles get toasted, sometimes by the thousands. Some farmers, in search of speed and efficiency, have even taken to flame-broiling them with tractor-mounted flamers. The potato plant can recover from this brief exposure to intense heat, but the beetles cannot.

Did somebody say beetles flambé?

A History of Dummerston, Vermont

A few weeks ago my wife brought home a book, a tag-sale special dated 1884, on the history of our town. I started reading *The History of Dummerston* by David Mansfield, and I got hooked. Here are a few things I learned.

On November 30, 1724, Colonel Joseph Kellogg and his scouting party were the first white men ever to visit Dummerston, Vermont. The colonel wrote in his journal, describing his equivalent of radar surveillance: "The next scout I sent up ye West River Mountain, and there to lodge on ye top and view evening and morning for smoakes, and thence up ye mountain at Great Falls and there also to lodge on ye top and view morning and evening for smoak; but these making no discovery of any enemy, returned."

According to the book, eleven years before this visit, in 1713, the tract of land that would eventually contain the towns of Brattleboro, Dummerston, and Putney had been granted to Connecticut by the colony of Massachusetts as part of a land swap. But Connecticut didn't really want southeastern Vermont, so in 1716 it was auctioned off to four men from Boston and Cambridge. Mr. Dummer was the oldest of the new owners, so the land was named Dummerston.

In 1741, it was determined that this land was actually part of New Hampshire, which incorporated the tract into three townships. The middle township, what is now Dummerston, was chartered as Fullum in 1753. The charter was issued to fifty-seven men in the name of King George II by the governor of New Hampshire. After setting aside two shares of the best land for the governor, as the charter required, the men divided the town into equal shares. The charter gave these men protection under the law, but it contained a number of conditions.

A meeting had to be held on the first Tuesday of every March to select town officers. Within the first five years, every grantee was required to cultivate five acres of land for every 100 acres. All pine trees fit to be made into masts for the royal navy were to be carefully preserved for that use. Rent for the first ten years was to be one ear of Indian corn annually; after that, every settler was to pay one shilling in rent for every 100 acres he owned.

Because of the French and Indian Wars, the grantees claimed they could not meet the timetable of the charter, so they applied for, and were granted, extensions.

According to Mansfield, Dummerston was the first town in Vermont to be settled by Anglo-Saxon descendants. The first white man to take up permanent residence in town was Captain John Kathan. Kathan had been born during his parents' passage to America, and he moved to Dummerston from Worcester, Massachusetts with his family in May of 1761. In November of 1762 they moved into a log house. You can imagine what that first winter must have been like without decent shelter. Over the next decade several dozen families settled permanently in the town.

In 1774 it was obvious that trouble was brewing, and this time it wasn't with the Indians. One of the settlers, Leonard Spaulding, was imprisoned for high treason against King George III. The townsfolk, accompanied by men from nearby towns, secured Mr. Spaulding's release from jail by physical means. The town clerk recorded the event as follows: "The plain truth is that the sons of freedom whose patience was worn out with the inhuman insults of the imps of power, grew quite sick of diving after redress in a legal way and finding that the law was made only for the emissaries of the British tyrant, resolved an easier method." The following month, the freeholders of Dummerston voted to assess the town a sum of money sufficient to procure a hundredweight of gunpowder, two hundredweight of lead, and 300 flints. The American Revolution was about to begin.

By 1850, less than a century after the first whites moved to town, the land had been tamed and had been widely put to agricultural use. That year, the people of Dummerston produced 3,300 pounds of maple sugar, had 1,600 head of cattle, harvested nearly 10,000 bushels of oats and rye, and made 45,000 pounds of butter and 14,000 pounds of cheese.

Given my newfound passion for local history, I'm looking forward to visiting the Vermont History Expo this fall, where the Windham County Historical Society will be featuring an exhibit on one of Dummerston's most interesting characters, Dr. John Wilson, who may have been the notorious criminal Captain Thunderbolt.

Corn in the USA

In 1492, Christopher Columbus visited what is now Cuba. He observed that a lot of land was sown to beans and to a kind of grain the Indians called maize, known to us as corn. Columbus took some of the grain back to Spain where it was grown as a garden curiosity. Within three decades this corn had made its way to Turkey, and it was grown so widely there that it became known as Turkish Corn, *corn* being the English term for cereal grains like wheat and barley.

A century later, when the Pilgrims landed, they found a large basket of corn buried under a pile of sand. Luckily they saved it until the following spring when Squanto, a friendly Native American—and in many ways the first extension agent—showed them how to plant it in hills, along with a few small herring for fertilizer.

Growing corn was nothing new in the New World; for thousands of years, it had been the principal food crop of tribes across the hemisphere. Corn was the backbone of the remarkable civilizations developed by the Aztecs in Mexico, the Mayas in Central America, and the Incas of Bolivia and Peru. It was also a staple food for tribes from Arizona to the Atlantic coast.

These people grew a great many different kinds of corn such as dent corn, flint corn, sweet corn, and popcorn. They also grew many different colors of corn including yellow, red, blue, and white. They had a special relationship with corn, and revered it. They had cultivated corn for such a long time, and it was so domesticated, that it could no longer reproduce itself unless its seed was gathered, planted, and tended by people. There is no wild corn.

Corn is a grass—it's in the same family of plants that includes the grasses in our lawns, small grains like rye and oats, as well as bamboo and sugar cane—but corn has the most unusual flowers in the family. At the top of the corn stalk are the male flowers, or tassels, that shed pollen. The female flowers, or ears, can be found on the side of the corn stalk. These ears are tufted with the sticky ends of many threads called the silk. Each thread of the silk is actually a part of a female flower called the style, and each style attaches to an individual ovary, which, once fertilized, develops into a seed or kernel. To accomplish fertilization, a microscopic pollen grain must grow a pollen tube inside the length of the silk until it reaches the ovary. Corn styles and corn pollen tubes are the longest in the plant kingdom.

In the United States today, corn is produced by 300,000 farmers who plant eighty million acres and harvest nearly ten billion bushels of kernels. That's 43 percent of all the corn grown in the world. A little over half the nation's crop is used to feed animals, almost a quarter of it is exported, and the rest goes into making a variety of products such as ethanol for fuel, high fructose corn syrup, and cereals.

In the last half-century, the acreage of corn planted in this country hasn't changed too much; it's about the same now as it was in 1950. But the yields have gone up 400 percent, to an average of 137 bushels an acre. Prices, on the other hand, have increased by just 33¢ a bushel over the past fifty years, from $1.32 in 1950 to $1.85 a bushel in 2000.

Buy Local Food and
Reduce Risk

Many reasons to buy local food are economic: Buying local circulates money in the community rather than exporting it, and it helps keep nearby farmers in business, too. Working farms not only provide us with food security and a pleasing landscape, they also attract tourism dollars. In Vermont, a relatively large proportion of our farms are organic, as compared to the rest of the country. Besides avoiding synthetic pesticides, these farms, by necessity, discover and refine nonchemical techniques for stewarding the soil and controlling pests.

From personal knowledge, I would bet that local crops, whether organic or conventional, are less likely to have pesticides on them than crops from major fruit- and vegetable-producing regions. The reasons are several: Vermont farmers use less pesticide because they run small, diversified family farms rather than large monocultural ones; we also don't have many months of warm humid weather that promotes pest problems. It also gets as cold as you-know-what here in the winter, which kills lots of pests naturally. And, finally, local crops stay out of a food-distribution system where post-harvest pesticides may be applied to protect produce during storage and travel.

Recent studies by the United States Department of Agriculture point to a noneconomic reason to buy local and organic fruits and vegetables: to minimize your risk of exposure to pesticide residues. The majority of fruits and vegetables in the commercial distribution system do have pesticide residues on them, according to those USDA studies, although detectable levels are for the most part extremely low. In a 1995 pesticide residue study, USDA collected 6,924 samples of apples, bananas, carrots, grapes, green beans, oranges, peaches, potatoes, spinach, canned and frozen corn, and sweet peas from distribution centers and warehouses in nine states. The products originated from thirty-nine states and seventeen countries; 16 percent of the products were imported. Analysis revealed that 65 percent of the samples had at least one pesticide residue, and there were two or more residues detected on 40 percent. However, less than 4 percent of all the samples had *illegal* levels of pesticide residue on them, a situation that's called a "violation of tolerance." Tolerances are the levels of pesticide residues that are legally allowed on foods. A violation occurs if residue levels exceed the tolerance, or if materials are found on the food that have no tolerance established, which basically means they were not supposed to be used at all. Almost all the violations found in this study were due to the latter, and only 10 percent of all the violations were on imported commodities, so we can't blame the problem on other countries.

Samples in this study were prepared using practices of the average consumer (apples and peaches washed and cored, bananas and oranges peeled, and other crops washed and stems removed if present). The samples were then analyzed for fifty-three different pesticides and twenty pesticide byproducts, based on an Environmental Protection Agency list of materials "whose toxicities and estimated dietary exposures indicate the need for more refined exposure estimates." The study searched for residues at the lowest detectable levels, which are far below the tolerances established by the EPA. Tolerances are usually expressed in parts per million, and some of the residues in this study were detected at parts per billion or less.

So what's the take-home message? This is a risky article to write, because people tend to have very different, strong reactions to such information. Consumers usually overreact to the risk, especially because pesticide residues are invisible and thus scarier than more tangible health risks. Farmers often feel defensive because most do indeed rely on pesticides to combat pests and produce the blemish-free produce that consumers demand. Farmers are only using products that industry and government have deemed safe, so why does the public take it out on them?

As a scientist, my rational conclusion is that the public should not freak out, because the risks implied here are very low in terms of a modern world full of health risks that include pumping your own gas, using art supplies, taking medicines, drinking alcohol or coffee, and other daily activities. It is also clear to me that agriculture can and must do a better job of reducing tolerance violations as well as the levels of legal pesticide residues on food.

As a parent of young children, though, my emotional conclusion is that these data are disturbing and the current food system is unacceptable. I do not want my kids eating *any* pesticides, and I don't care how many agencies tell me it's safe for them to do so. What really gets me mad is that our cheap-food policy and lack of investment in sustainable agriculture research is not only putting our kids at risk, it is putting family farms out of business and squandering precious resources like clean water. For what? So we can save a few more dollars on food expenditures that are already the lowest in the industrialized world? But the key to positive change is a transition that does not hurt farmers by simply removing pest control tools without developing cleaner and more effective alternatives. Integrated Pest Management (IPM) is one first step, and consumers should support IPM produce, but there's a long way to go. If you really want change, lobby your legislators and policy makers to improve funding for progressive research, extension, and education that develops and promotes nontoxic farming techniques such as biological insect control, disease-resistant varieties, and mechanical weed-control tools.

Finally, don't stop eating fruits and vegetables—they're good for you. Many studies document the benefits, but it does seem like a little more peeling or washing may be a good idea. And by all means buy local. Buy organic, too, but buying local is the most important step to supporting a healthier food system. Supporting corporate organic farms far away is not the way to secure a safe food supply and a sustainable agriculture in the long term.

GMO Contamination

For farmers who grow organic field crops for wholesale markets, the immediate threat of genetic engineering and genetically modified organisms, or GMOs, can be summed up in one word: contamination. With alarming frequency, organically- and conventionally-grown soy, corn, and canola crops have tested positive for the presence of foreign genetic material because of cross-pollination, co-mingling of seed stock, or the difficulty of completely cleaning out a combine between harvests on different farms. Our farming and food-handling systems are simply not set up to assure that genetically engineered, or transgenic, crops will be segregated from their organic counterparts during harvest, handling, transport, and milling. As a result, low-level contamination seems almost impossible to avoid.

This contamination is threatening organic wholesale markets at home and abroad. The Organic Federation of Australia has declared that contamination from transgenic crops in the United States has spread to such a degree that it cannot verify the purity of imported organic ingredients.

Farm Verified Organic seconds that assertion. This North Dakota based certification agency says that the genetic pollution of American commodities is now so pervasive that they believe it is no longer possible for farmers in North America to source seed that is free from it. Their investigations of crops from the 2000 harvest indicate that virtually all of the seed corn in the U.S. is contaminated with at least a trace of genetically engineered material. Even the organic lots showed traces of biotech varieties.

The widespread adoption of genetically modified crops in the U.S. is making it especially difficult to ensure that grain is not being contaminated with GMOs as it is handled and transported from the field to the end customer. As it stands now, all major seed companies refuse to guarantee that their seeds are free from any genetic contamination. And if that's not bad enough, the next concern of organic farmers is the question of whether the foundation or parent seed that is used for breeding non-GMO varieties can be guaranteed to meet a level of no more than 1-percent contamination.

Since a ban on transgenic crops probably won't happen anytime soon, organic certification agencies are working to establish a maximum-tolerance level for GMOs in organic crops. Currently, there is no universal standard among certification programs. Most people agree that it wouldn't be practical to require organic products to be 100 percent free of GMOs. The recent experience with Star Link, a bioengineered corn that was not intended for human consumption but nevertheless became widespread at low levels throughout the food system, suggests that if organic certifiers insist on zero-percent contamination, there probably won't be any certified organic corn at all.

The planting of millions of acres of transgenic crops year after year is likely to lead to the presence of more and more genetic contamination of organic crops. This could require raising the tolerance levels. Whether the organic stamp of approval would then become something of a joke is open to debate.

But we should remember that organic standards have never been based on testing of food for purity; instead, they have always been based on production methods. That means that testing for any kind of residue, whether it's pesticides or genetic contamination, is not part of the normal certification process. The problem is that more and more companies that use organic crops in their products are asking for genetic tests to assure the integrity of their ingredients. As it stands now, when those tests come back positive, organic farmers will be left holding the bag.

George Aiken

August 20 is a special day because it's the birthday of George Aiken, a man who spent a lifetime in public service to Vermont and a politician who exemplified the integrity, independence, and straight talk that seems all too rare in politics today.

The first few things I learned about George Aiken are probably the best-known parts of his legendary record. One was his outrageous yet commonsense proposal to end our entanglement in Viet Nam: Declare victory and get out. Another was the cost of his final campaign for the senate in 1968: $17. Then I learned that he was a farmer and a horticulturist by trade, and that got me hooked. I started digging deeper into the story of Aiken's life and his legislative legacy.

Aiken was born in my hometown of Dummerston in 1892. From the get-go he was a leader, and he was master of the Putney Grange by the time he was 18. Then, starting when he was 28, he served fifteen years as a school director for the town of Putney before being elected to the Vermont House of Representatives in 1931, where he soon became Speaker of the House. After that, he was the lieutenant governor for two years, then governor for four years, and then, in 1940, he went on to serve in the United States Senate, a position he held for a remarkable thirty-four years.

As a senator, George Aiken was always looking out for the interests of Vermonters, and rural Vermonters in particular. He supported the Rural Electrification Administration, against the wishes of his own political party, because it directly improved life down on the farm, and farms were what the rural life in Vermont was all about. He worked for a decade to get the St. Lawrence Seaway built because he felt it would lower the cost of electricity and imported grain for Vermonters. Aiken also fought to protect Vermont farmland by defeating measures that would have flooded it in order to provide hydroelectric power for utilities in southern New England. But Aiken was not against all new power sources, and especially not if the power went to Vermonters. In 1959, as a member of the Joint Committee on Atomic Energy, he helped place the Vermont Yankee nuclear power plant in Vernon because he saw nuclear power as an alternative to fossil fuels.

While that action may not endear him to environmentalists, Aiken did do a lot to protect the environment. In 1947 he guided the first comprehensive federal pesticide controls through Congress, and in 1972 he worked to improve these regulations. He secured passage of the Eastern Wilderness Act, earning him the title, "Father of the Eastern Wilderness." That law went into effect in 1975, establishing 200,000 acres of wilderness held in fifteen different areas, two of them in Vermont. Aiken spoke eloquently of the need to set aside some wild areas east of the Mississippi while it was still possible to do so.

As a member of the Labor and Public Welfare Committee in the 1940s and 1950s, Aiken did a lot to help families in need, often helping agriculture at the same time. He guided many bills through the Senate, including the Food Allotment Bill, which distributed surplus agricultural commodities to low-income people. He was a cosponsor of the Food Stamp program, the Hot Lunch program, and the School Milk program. For more than half a century, these programs have assisted needy families across the country. In 1969 Aiken helped establish WIC, the Women, Infants, and Children program that provides food assistance to nursing and expectant mothers.

George Aiken was a farmer, even if he wasn't a typical one—he owned a wildflower farm. He had a passion for growing things, and he authored two books on horticulture: *Pioneering with Wildflowers*, and *Pioneering with Fruits and Berries*. Perhaps it was his connection to the land and the people who lived off it that motivated him so strongly to look after them both.

And maybe it was his experience in dealing with nature on a day-to-day basis that gave him a dose of humility and a talent for diplomacy. But he also had a sense of humor, and dedicated his book on wildflowers to "Peter Rabbit, in the hope that flattery will accomplish what traps and guns have failed to do, and that the little rascal will let our plants alone from this time on."

A Pumpkin Primer

The pumpkin is an odd vegetable. In botanical terms, it's really a fruit, as are all vegetables that contain seeds in a fleshy package, like tomatoes or cucumbers. But what's really odd is that the more popular pumpkins get, the less people eat them. Everyone wants to carve a jack-o'-lantern, but few people make pumpkin pie anymore. In other words, the pumpkin has gone from being a basic food to being just another pretty face.

When the first Europeans arrived on our shores, pumpkins and squash were being cultivated by almost every tribe in North, Central, and South America. Native Americans used them in soup, boiled them, baked them, made them into cakes, and dried them for winter use. The seeds were roasted and salted, just as they are today. The white settlers soon learned to grow pumpkins and ate them often in desserts, stews, and soups.

Both pumpkins and squashes were called *askoot-asquash* by the Algonquin Indians. The word *pumpkin*, however, comes from an old French word meaning *ripe, mellow*, and *cooked by the sun*. Pumpkins are believed to have originated in North America, and seeds from related plants that date back over 7,000 years have been found in Mexico. Now pumpkins are grown all over the world and on all continents except Antarctica.

Pumpkins are in the *Cucurbita* family of plants that also includes squash and cucumbers, and there are actually several different species of pumpkins. *Cucurbita moschata* includes the pumpkins used for canning. They tend to be oblong and have tan skins; butternut squash is another members of this species. *Cucurbita pepo* is the jack-o'-lantern and miniature pumpkin type; most summer squashes and zucchini are also members of this species. *Cucurbita maxima* includes Hubbard squash, buttercup squash, and most winter squashes, as well as those beasts of the pumpkin patch, giant pumpkins. These are grown from varieties like 'Prize Winner,' 'Big Max,' and the famous 'Atlantic Giant,' which has produced the heavyweight fruits of record. While some people waited years for the stock market to break 10,000, for growers of giant pumpkins it was the 1,000-pound barrier that seemed unbreakable. Then, in 1996, it was broken twice. Since then seventeen pumpkins have officially weighed in at over half a ton, and as I write this the most recent world record is 1,140 pounds, achieved in 2000 by Dave Stelts of Leetonia, Ohio.

Of course even the largest pumpkin starts with a flower, usually sometime in July. First come the male flowers that often proliferate for a week or two before the first females show up. Male flowers contain pollen, and are formed on a thin stem that shoots up several inches to a foot above the vine. Female flowers are easy to identify because they are close to the vine and have what looks like a tiny pumpkin between the stem and the flower. Insects must transfer pollen from male to female flowers; otherwise, the baby pumpkin below the female flower will shrivel and die. And even though the honeybee population is down, struggling with parasitic mites, many other insects are also effective pollinators, particularly native squash bees and even the cucumber beetle, which also damages pumpkin leaves and fruit.

Once the fruit has set, the pumpkins grow rapidly. Some medium-sized varieties will be ready to harvest early in September, which is good, since consumers seem to be ready to buy pumpkins earlier and earlier. Just as the Christmas season now begins after Thanksgiving, preparations for Halloween commence soon after Labor Day.

The origin of Halloween dates back 2,000 years to a Celtic event that celebrated the harvest and honored the dead. Costumes were donned and sacrifices were burned. Halloween spread throughout Europe in the seventh century and came to include the lighting of carved gourds and turnips with scary faces to ward off evil spirits. Sometime along the way, people switched to carving pumpkins, which were both larger and much easier to carve than turnips.

Integrated Pest Management

Pickled beets are one of my favorites. The wife and kids hate them, so I dine on these delicacies alone, sneaking mouthfuls of round red roots late at night when no one will scrunch up their face at me in disgust. It's not easy being a sneaky beet eater, because there's always some evidence of my culinary infraction—unavoidably, a few drops of beet juice stain the wooden cutting board, and in the morning I'm caught red-handed.

My latest heist was a jar of New York beets, and the label had an outline of the Empire State on it. Next to this geographic reminder was the acronym IPM, which stands for Integrated Pest Management. The back of the jar explained that IPM is a set of farming methods that minimize the use of pesticides; the jar went on to tell me that not only were these beets good for me, they were also better for the environment.

This news made me stop in midbite. Actually, I felt better about the beets *before* I was reminded they were grown with pesticides. Don't get me wrong: IPM has been great at helping farmers spray their crops less, mostly by improving the timing of applications so that fewer sprays do a better job of controlling insects and diseases. And IPM farmers also try to select the least-toxic pesticides that will do the job. But for most consumers, ignorance is bliss. We want perfect looking, pest-free, inexpensive produce, and we don't want to think about how it gets that way.

The reality is that we have a food system that relies on many chemicals to accommodate intensive, large-scale production on farms far away from consumers. Our government has invested in this system, researchers support it, lobbyists promote it, and corporations profit from it. And while much effort goes into making sure this system is as safe as it can be, the long-term costs of this system are not honestly accounted for, leaving future generations to pick up the tab.

The result? Compared to the rest of the world, our food is cheap, uniform, and abundant to the point of oversupply. Small farms have difficulty competing on price. There is little credit given in the marketplace for nonchemical farming practices, and most farmers have come to rely on a variety of chemicals so they can achieve the necessary yields and quality standards that allow them to survive. As I roll a baby beet from one cheek to the other, I can't help but think that there's got to be a better way.

In fact, many farmers are working on one. They're seeking ecological rather than industrial solutions to their problems. They're diversifying, recycling nutrients, rotating crops, and using biological pest controls. Some of these farmers are organic and some aren't, but they're all trying to manage their farms as a system, rather than as a set of isolated problems. Vermont offers some advantages in this regard: We have lots of biological diversity, lots of a deep-seated stewardship ethic, and our thirty- and forty-below winters spare us some of the pest problems that arise in warmer regions. So buying Vermont-grown food not only makes economic sense, it's an investment in environmentally-friendly farming.

Of course, our farmers can do even better, but they don't need to be punished or threatened for using the current tools of the trade. They need support from the government and academia to help them develop more and better agro-ecological management techniques.

And that's starting to happen. For example, at the USDA Appalachian Fruit Research Station in West Virginia, scientists have set up complex orchards with mixtures of apples, pears, and flowering ground covers to see what happens to pests and beneficial insects. In New York, reams of data are being collected from organic and conventional vegetable farms to better understand the relationships among soil, crop, and pest management practices. These studies are a good start, and we can hope that they're just the beginning of a transition from IPM—Integrated Pest Management—to EFM—Ecological Farm Management.

Kindle Farm
for At-Risk Youth

K indle Farm is growing an unusual product: self-esteem for young people. Located in Newfane, Vermont, Kindle Farm is a school that works with children who haven't been successful in a traditional public school setting. The students at Kindle Farm have usually experienced trauma or disruption in their lives, and they often have a mix of academic and behavioral disabilities. Many of them have a negative sense of self and lack trust in other people. Kindle Farm combines academics, recreation, traditional therapy, and experiential education to meet the needs of these students.

Kindle Farm was started in 1996 with founder Bob Bursky and three students, and it now has about thirty instructors and aides that work with seventy kids of all ages. It receives funding from local public school districts. The vocational program for high school students is especially exciting—ten students work on the school's 100-acre farm using a hands-on curriculum that's organized around farm activities. Math, science, English, and history lessons are tied directly to gardening, carpentry, mechanics, and the history of the property. The students run a half-acre market garden where they grow vegetables, flowers, and herbs. They recently erected a greenhouse, and then built their own post-and-beam roadside stand from scratch.

The students are learning about composting, soil fertility, garden planning, and crop production. But that's not all: Students also take turns operating the farm stand, weighing the vegetables, computing sales, and replenishing inventory. The market operation enables students to learn about running a business. They keep records of income, expenses, and accounts payable, and each student maintains and balances his or her own financial books throughout the year.

While much of the produce grown by the vocational program is sold at the stand and to local stores, a lot of the harvest is also used for daily lunches and cooking classes at the school. The kids help others in the community, too, when they deliver excess vegetables to the Drop-In Center, a program that gives food and clothes to low-income families.

Carpentry is part of the hands-on educational program, too. Because of a lack of maintenance and the passage of time—the structure is 230 years old—repairing Kindle Farm's old barn was a challenging project. The barn had severe water damage and a tree had grown up in one corner of the building. The restoration project allowed students to learn the proper use of hand tools and to gain an understanding of colonial post-and-beam construction. They also learned about modern power tools and building techniques. Fractions, decimals, and physics were encountered as day-to-day construction problems were solved.

Kindle Farm does more that develop technical skills; there's also a focus on leadership development as a means of reducing risky behavior. The vocational students mentor students from other Kindle Farm school programs. They lead activities, instruct their peers in proper work technique, and occasionally give presentations to groups of students visiting from other schools.

Eric Shearing is in charge of the vocational program at Kindle Farm. Although he was raised on a successful dairy farm in western New York, he thought he'd left farming when, after college, he got into non-profit educational work. Then he got involved with horticulture and small-scale farming, and teaching at Kindle Farm has allowed him to blend his passions for education and agriculture.

Eric said, "For many of these kids, the opportunities for success have been limited. With our small groups, we can fine-tune our program to meet their interests. We get them mentally and physically engaged in a task, and at the end of the day they can turn around and see the fruits of their labor. It gives them a sense of accomplishment, and with that comes self-confidence. That's what we're trying to build in these kids: The realization that they have legitimate skills to offer to the rest of society. Our farm has created the opportunity to interact with the public, and the students are getting positive feedback from the community. For some of these kids, such moments have been few and far between."

After 9/11

It's been many weeks since that unspeakable event, and everyone's still talking about it. I'd rather not mention it. Let's just get over it and move on, shall we? But, like a lot of people, I've gone through so many feelings, felt so many emotions, that I'm just not done processing what has happened, trying to understand what it means and what has changed.

In the first week of this new age, I had a hard time driving. I kept getting all choked up, thanks to the news on National Public Radio. It wasn't the headlines that got to me, but the real people being interviewed, talking about the terror they experienced, the loved ones they lost, and the heroism they witnessed. I found myself fighting back tears every time *Morning Edition or All Things Considered* rolled around. Why I fought them back I'm not sure—I mean, alone in the car, it's not like I risked being embarrassed.

Then, stationary at home, I felt a different sadness talking to my kids about what they already knew everyone was talking about. My children are young, so the conversation was pretty simple. The gist of it was that a few bad people did some very horrible things, a lot of good people got hurt, and everyone's upset.

"Daddy?" my five-year old asked, "Did those bad men ask permission to take those airplanes?"

Now I didn't know whether to laugh or cry. Trying to explain terrorism to a child has got to be one of the all-time lows of parenting.

And the conversations haven't gotten a whole lot easier. A couple of weeks ago my eight-year-old asked, "Are we having a war?"

"Well, we're dropping bombs in a country where some bad people are living."

"Is that good?" he asked.

Hmm, I thought, *do you mean good in the sense of politically and military necessity, or good in terms of spiritual and karmic well-being?* Leave to a kid to cut to the chase of a difficult question. I miss the simple questions he used to ask, like *How does gravity work?*

To cope, I've developed a little mantra, a simple plan of action. The way to fight insanity is with sanity. In other words, I keep on doing what I do, I try to do it well, and work toward some end that is good. From the simple chores and pleasures at home to more complicated professional endeavors, it helps to be true to yourself, to be good to others, and to honor the sanctity of life by living it to its fullest. Maybe that sounds corny or simplistic, but frankly I don't know what else to tell myself.

Connections to the land and nature have been a source of special comfort and equanimity for me, and, I suspect, for many of you. We still have the uncomplicated grace and meaning of outdoor tasks. In the garden, harvesting fall crops and sowing oats for a winter cover never felt better. Raking leaves amidst the glorious foliage, the changing of the seasons, has been especially welcome and familiar. The stacking of wood, the splitting of kindling, the draining of hoses all seem reassuringly useful and sensible.

I would guess that many people are examining their lives a little more closely for what gives them meaning. For some, that may be a hard process. For many farmers, it's a no-brainer. Farmers tend to be blessed with a clarity of purpose in their role as providers of food and fiber and stewards of the land; they seem to engage in their livelihood with little doubt about its usefulness, despite endless cycles of ups and downs.

At a recent Windham County Farm Bureau meeting, David Major, the county president and a sheep farmer from Westminster, articulated this well as he reviewed the past year. He said, "Given recent events, it is a comfort to reflect on things agricultural. Even if we had to shovel more snow than I've seen in my lifetime, even if we watched half our forage disappear before an invasion of armyworms, followed by a severe summer drought, even if we had to slog through an economy unfriendly to farming, none of these plagues compare to the worldwide disaster caused by a few dozen men. In a funny way, the ordinary challenges we face as farmers are welcome. When my animals get out, these days I catch myself breathing a small sigh of relief to see they're up to as much trouble as they ever were." Then he thanked everyone who helps keep our agricultural community alive.

2002

Clover: Not Just the
Vermont State Flower

Livestock farmers depend on two families of plants: grasses, like small grains and corn, and legumes, like alfalfa and clover. Alfalfa was widely produced in the Roman Empire, and other legumes like beans and peas have been grown for thousands of years in various parts of the world. But through most of history, farm animals have been raised primarily on grass.

Then, around 1500 A.D., red clover began to be cultivated in Italy and Spain as a forage crop. From there it went to Holland, and then to England. Colonists brought red clover to North America, and now it's grown on eight to ten million acres nationwide.

In 1894, red clover became the state flower of Vermont, in tribute to its importance for pastures, hay, and honey production. Red clover, like many clovers, can't bear seeds unless it's been fertilized by insects carrying pollen from one blossom to another. There are many improved varieties of red clover, including a tall variety called 'Mammoth' clover, used as a soil improver.

White clover, or Dutch clover, is common in North American pastures and lawns. It's a low-spreading plant just a few inches high, and its pure white blossoms are rich in nectar and a major source of honey. 'Alsike' clover, named for a place in Sweden, is a perennial that grows from one to two feet tall. It's hardier than red clover and grows in wetter soils. Its blossoms turn from white to a rose color.

Legumes, like clover, are an important part of livestock feed because they contain a lot of protein. A healthy diet for all livestock, whether horses, cattle, sheep, or poultry, includes a blend of protein and carbohydrate. Nitrogen is a key ingredient of protein, and legumes have two ways of getting their nitrogen.

Like other plants they can take it up from the soil but, unlike other plants, they can also get it from the air, and they do this with the help of bacteria. They need help because even though air contains 78 percent nitrogen gas, it's chemically unavailable to plants. Certain bacteria are able to get at that nitrogen and turn it into a form that plants can use, but the bacteria can't photosynthesize, so they need a source of energy. Well, leave it to evolution to work out a deal. The arrangement, called symbiotic nitrogen fixation, happens when the bacteria form nodules on the roots of legumes, providing them with available nitrogen in exchange for a steady diet of carbon compounds.

Usually if you pull up some clover or alfalfa, you'll see these little nodules sprinkled all along the roots. Crack one open with your fingernail. The pink color inside comes from a kind of hemoglobin, similar to the hemoglobin that makes your blood red. I'll bet you didn't know you had something in common with a legume root nodule, but you do.

A Stroll Down Main Street

It's been said that Vermont has more cows than people, and while that's not true, the ratio is impressive. With 159,000 dairy cows and 600,000 people, it comes out to about a quarter of a cow, or almost 400 pounds of cow per person. So, at least on a weight basis, Vermont really does have more cows than people.

Holsteins are the most popular and the largest dairy cow in Vermont, and they give a lot of milk. The result is that Vermont's 1,500 dairy farms produce 2.6 billion pounds of milk annually. To celebrate all this milk, all these cows, and all our hardworking dairy farmers, June is Dairy Month. And this year there's a unique event planned: On June 8, cows go on parade. That's right—for an hour on Saturday morning, Brattleboro's Main Street will become a bovine boulevard, closed to traffic while thirty heifers hoof it from one end of downtown to the other. This event, billed as the "Strolling of the Heifers," is Vermont's answer to the running of the bulls in Spain, although it's going to be much mellower.

The heifers, which are cows that have not yet had a calf, won't be loose on the streets, and they won't be running. In fact, they'll be on leads, guided by handlers who will be sure the animals are treated humanely. And these are special cows—they come from the Putney School dairy, and they're used to being among people and walking around at agricultural fairs.

The cows will start out, fittingly, from the world headquarters of the Holstein Association, a nonprofit organization with 44,000 members who breed, milk, and market Holstein cattle. Nineteen million Holsteins have their genealogy and performance records on file in Brattleboro. Fortunately, they won't all be strolling up Main Street.

After the parade comes a celebration of local agriculture. Samples of farm delicacies, including cheeses and maple products, will be available. There will also be live music in the streets and readings of poems and stories about cows and farms. Another highlight will be our congressional delegation engaging in the ultimate political showdown, a milking contest.

If you can't make it to Brattleboro, there's another way to celebrate farming during June. Open Farm Day, an annual event that invites visitors to come to the farms and look around, is sponsored by the Vermont Department of Agriculture's Ag in the Classroom program. It's a day to learn about local farms and local food production up close and personal. Participating farms include orchards, vineyards, vegetable farms, and sugar houses, as well as dairy farms. There are tours, refreshments, and hands-on activities, and all of it is free.

So whether you stroll with heifers, visit farms, eat local cheese, or just drink milk, June is the month to celebrate Vermont's dairy farms.

Garden Optimism

Now that summer's almost here, optimism abounds: Red Sox fans think World Series, students hope for straight As, and gardeners dream of their crops to come.

My seedlings are sown, my soil is fertile, and my thumbs are green once again. Forget bygone weather woes and pests. Optimism is the engine of horticulture in Vermont.

These are my plans for the coming season: After a wobbly start, temperatures will settle in for the summer at about 75 degrees and stay there. Rainfall will be uniformly distributed—an inch or two every week, between Mondays and Fridays. Sunny weekends. There may be hail, flood, or drought in other states, but we'll have none of that. The season will stretch on into autumn, the first frost holding off until after a bumper crop of fall raspberries.

Japanese beetles and European corn borer will promote international harmony by doing no damage on these shores. Blight, wilt, scab, and smut will not live up to their names. Birds and bunnies will find enough food in the wild. And the local deer herd will enjoy a menu that doesn't include cultivated crops.

Just in case these fantasies don't come true, I am making some practical plans, too, trying a few new things in the garden this year to tilt nature's balance in my favor. I put up a deer fence around the flower garden, and I'm going to put trickle irrigation in the vegetable garden, attached to the outdoor spigot. For a hundred dollars I got all the components I need to save me from standing around like a human sprinkler. This year, I'm also swearing off manure that's not fully composted, since it usually contains a gazillion weed seeds. Instead, I'll be mixing in a couple of inches of well-made compost into each bed before planting annuals, or spreading a layer around the perennials.

My garden security will screen out the terror of flea beetles, potato beetles, and cabbage maggot flies. I'll be covering many early-season crops with a floating row cover that lets sun and water in but keeps pests out. Then I'll follow with biological warfare by applying *Bacillus thuringiensis* the moment young caterpillar pests arrive. On my apples I'll use a nontoxic insecticide made from kaolin clay to suppress plum curculio.

For noxious weeds (is there any other kind?) I'm planning on hand-to-hand combat. I've sharpened my trusty old hoes and I've even ordered a special collinear hoe with a thin blade for cutting off small weeds in tight places.

Of course, the joy of gardening comes not just from triumphs over weather and critters. There's also the pleasure of trying something new. This year I'll be checking out edamame, also known as vegetable soybean. I've ordered multicolored radishes, red and yellow carrots, and purple tomatillos. At the end of summer, I'll plant strawberry plugs for harvest the following spring.

Some of my plans will bear fruit, and others may wilt, but one thing I know for sure: By the end of next winter, I'll be dreaming of the perfect garden once again.

Ten Reasons to Buy Local Food

Winter in Vermont is great for a lot of things, but growing fruits and vegetables isn't one of them; when it comes to eating fresh, local produce, it's pretty much feast or famine around here. Right now it's May, my storage crops are long gone, and I'm eagerly anticipating the bounty that's soon to come—greens, asparagus, zucchini, and broccoli, along with sweet corn, strawberries, and other crops that my kids actually like. Blueberries, melons, carrots, and more, nurtured from the not-so-long-ago frozen tundra.

Vermont is blessed with a variety of farms that raise fruits and vegetables, flowers and herbs, and animals of all kinds. Our farmers are dedicated to stewardship and committed to quality. And while they love what they do, they aren't doing it for entertainment. They need to make a living. As consumers, we should support local farmers by buying their products. Here are ten reasons why:

Local food tastes better. The crops are picked at their peak, and farmstead products like cheeses are hand-crafted for the best flavor. Food imported from far away is older, has traveled on trucks or planes, and has sat in warehouses before it finally gets to you.

Local produce is better for you. The shorter the time between the farm and your table, the less likely it is that nutrients will be lost from fresh food.

Local food preserves genetic diversity. In the modern agricultural system, plant varieties are chosen for their ability to ripen uniformly, withstand harvesting, survive packing, and last a long time on the shelf, so there is limited genetic diversity in large-scale production. Smaller local farms, in contrast, often grow many different varieties to provide a long harvest season, in an array of colors and flavors.

Local food is safe. There's a unique kind of assurance that comes from looking a farmer in the eye at farmers' market or driving by the fields where your food comes from. Local farmers aren't anonymous and they take their responsibility to the consumer seriously.

Local food supports local families. The wholesale prices that farmers get for their products are low, often near the cost of production. Local farmers who sell directly to consumers cut out the middleman and get full retail price for their food, which helps farm families stay on the land.

Local food builds community. When you buy direct from a farmer, you're engaging in a time-honored connection between eater and grower. Knowing farmers gives you insight into the seasons, the land, and your food. In many cases, it gives you access to a place where your children and grandchildren can go to learn about nature and agriculture.

Local food preserves open space. When farmers get paid more for their products by marketing locally, they're less likely to sell their farmland for development. When you buy locally grown food, you're doing something proactive to preserve our agricultural landscape.

Local food keeps taxes down. According to several studies, farms contribute more in taxes than they require in services, whereas most other kinds of development contribute less in taxes than the cost of the services they require.

Local food benefits the environment and wildlife. Well-managed farms conserve fertile soil and clean water in our communities. The farm environment is a patchwork of fields, meadows, woods, ponds, and buildings that provide habitat for wildlife.

Local food is an investment in the future. By supporting local farmers today, you are helping to ensure that there will be farms in your community tomorrow.

— Adapted from the "Growing for Market" newsletter,
Lawrence, Kansas

Child Care in Vermont

It was a graduation ceremony like no other.

There wasn't much pomp or circumstance, but there was plenty of joy as the graduates filed into the room. Actually, they ran into the room. Then they sat in a circle and sang songs. This was my son's graduation from nursery school, and was cause for celebration, indeed.

Preschool child care has had enormous value to my family. Because of it, the kids got a jump on their formal education, good behavior was reinforced, and they had fun. My wife and I were able to go to work, confident that our children were well cared for, even loved.

We were lucky. Our child-care providers are saints: patient, creative, reliable, and completely committed to their little charges. They're so good that they won the Windham County Child Care Award. It turns out there are many saints working in child care, meeting an essential need of thousands of families in our communities. In fact, a new report, "The Economic Impact of Vermont's Child Care Industry," describes just how important child care is. More than 37,000 Vermont parents rely on child care so they can work. These parents earn a billion dollars annually, and pay $100 million in income taxes. Half of all the businesses in Vermont employ people with children in child care.

In addition to enabling people to work, the economic impact of child care as an industry in Vermont is $426 million a year. If that industry were a single employer it would be one of our largest, with 5,000 employees.

But high-quality child care isn't just good for grownups; it's also good for kids. It enhances brain development and prepares children to do well in school. Studies show that providing at-risk children with high-quality early learning programs reduces the chance that they'll engage in criminal activities later in life. An ounce of attention is worth a pound of cure.

For such a valuable service, though, child care sure is undervalued. Despite the fact that Vermont parents pay an average of $5,000 a year per child, these fees don't cover the full cost of quality childcare. The government chips in some support but it's not enough, and the result is that child-care workers in Vermont earn an average of just $7.60 an hour. Almost two-thirds of child-care providers can't afford health coverage for their employees. These low wages and poor benefits result in a high turnover of child care providers, and, in the meantime, there's a child-care shortage. The regulated child-care system meets only 65 percent of the need, and demand is expected to grow by 12 percent over the next decade. Finding child care is especially difficult for parents working nonstandard hours.

Public and private investment in child care is a no-brainer, and we need more of it to improve our economy, enhance our children's futures, and offer child-care providers the respect they deserve.

So—is it snack time yet?

A Sense of Place

She was just eighteen, and she was a smuggler.

There was a war going on in Europe, and she was bringing farm-fresh butter from the countryside into the big city. You weren't supposed to do that, but she needed the money for her family to survive. So she combined entrepreneurship and bravery. She was my grandmother.

I remember her telling me this story with humility, and with a sane acceptance of an insane world: "You do what you got to do." Then, twenty years later, there was another war. Armies were on the move, economies were collapsing, neighbors were disappearing in the night. It was time to pull up roots and go to America. Once again she showed a combination of bravery, foresight, and faith. A little luck and a letter from an American sponsor helped, too.

She had a funny habit of pinching the skin of the back of her hand as she talked, examining its lost resilience, watching it testify to her nine decades of life. "I don't know what happened," she said. "Just the other day I was a teenager. Now I'm an old lady."

She spoke in what the grandkids called *germlish*, a peculiar mix of German and English. Even though she only had an elementary school education, she was sharp as a tack, a graduate of the school of hard knocks. She did her postgraduate work on American language and culture by watching the soap operas. Every day.

And when she wasn't assimilating, she was cooking.

People who have lived with food shortages tend to enjoy cooking in a way that most of us will never know. That woman revered food, and the way she prepared meals involved a fondling of ingredients that verged on the pornographic. I mean, we've all squeezed a cantaloupe and kneaded bread dough now and again, but my grandmother *poked* and *pulled* and *flattened* and *rolled* food the way a cat scratches at fleas, with vigor and abandon.

Then she watched as you ate, a smile on her face, sharing your pleasure in every bite. But she wasn't easily satisfied. "What's the matter, you don't eat?" she'd exclaim, just when you thought you'd burst.

She loved this country, and she loved it in a special way. Her homeland was torn apart, the communities of her youth destroyed. But in America there was stability, opportunity, and liberty.

She had a powerful sense of place, but it wasn't the comfortable kind that comes when generations reside in the same location and people connect to the land like it was the back of their hand. Her sense of place came from losing that connection, crossing an ocean, and discovering a country where her family could start all over again.

Tomato Tales

What a year it was for tomatoes. I should know, since I grow about a dozen different kinds to hedge my bets. This season, they all paid off.

The greenhouse types did well, of course, because they were protected from the elements. But in the field, where the weather usually wreaks havoc, a dry summer kept diseases at bay and the frost was so late in coming that the harvest continued until the middle of October, about a month longer than usual.

That meant there were plenty of ugly but delicious 'Brandywines,' an heirloom variety. The 'Sun Gold' cherry tomatoes produced a lot of tasty yellow fruit, but they tended to split with the irregular rainfall. My favorite this year was 'Matt's Wild Cherry,' a very sweet and very small fruited variety that grows wild in Mexico, where the tomato was domesticated.

Like its relative the potato, the tomato originated in South America. Thousands of years ago, the people there began to cultivate a vining plant with little sour red berries. Over the centuries the ancestral tomato was carried from the Inca civilization in Peru to the Maya of Central America and then to the Toltecs in Mexico. Their Aztec conquerors called the plant *tomatl*, and their conquerors, the Spaniards, called it *tomate*.

The Conquistadors brought the tomato to Europe in the 1600s, where it was embraced by Spaniards and Italians. Northern Europeans were more suspicious, thought it might be poisonous, and only grew it for decoration, although some felt it was an aphrodisiac and began calling it the *love apple*. The tomato arrived in America in the late 1700s, along with all of the myths surrounding it. Because it resembled the other nightshades, it's easy to see why many people continued to think that it was poisonous. Adventuresome gardeners like Thomas Jefferson helped it gain in popularity. By 1835, tomatoes were widely eaten. Today, the tomato is our second-most-popular vegetable after the potato, and Americans consume an average of eighty-eight pounds per person each year. Processed products like tomato sauce, salsa, and ketchup account for 80 percent of our tomato consumption.

Surprisingly, recent research shows that heating tomatoes for commercial processing actually increases their antioxidant activity. Antioxidants are chemicals that protect aging bodies from stresses that can cause disease. Many fruits and vegetables are loaded with antioxidants. Blueberries, red grapes, and cranberries have the highest antioxidant activity among fruit, and tomatoes are surpassed only by garlic and broccoli among the vegetables.

Of course, in botanical terms, the tomato actually is a fruit because it contains seeds. But in 1893 the U.S. Supreme Court ruled that the tomato was a vegetable, and it's never looked back. That ruling protected U.S. tomato growers from foreign markets, since at the time there was an import tax on vegetables, but not fruits.

The Organic Police
Come Knocking

The siren stopped and there was a knock at the door.

"Who's there?"

"The Organic Police."

I rose from reading my seed catalogs at the kitchen table and opened the door.

A young man showed me some official papers and a badge. He fit my image of an organic policeman, if I'd ever thought about it—L.L. Bean pullover, Birkenstocks, sideburns just a little too long. He tossed his ponytail to the side and pulled a clipboard from his backpack.

"What's the problem?" I asked innocently.

"We have a report that you're selling vegetables and calling them organic, but they're not certified. That's been illegal since October 21, 2002."

"I do call my vegetables organic," I said, "but the national organic standards say I'm exempt from certification because I sell less than $5,000 worth a year."

"I know that," he replied, "but you still have to prove you're following the standards. I'm here to inspect your documentation."

"I thought the feds weren't going to visit any farms," I complained. "Only local certifying agencies."

"We're making an exception for you," was the gruff response. "To show that the United States Department of Agriculture cares about the integrity of organic food."

I went back to the kitchen and pointed to a shoebox stuffed full of papers on top of the fridge. "It's all in there," I said.

"Okay. Let's start with your organic production plan. We need a description of your farm practices as well as every material that was applied to the soil, crops, or livestock."

I let out a gasp, but then remembered. "Wait," I said. "Doesn't the rule say I can substitute another state or federal regulatory plan for my organic plan? Well, I've got my Act 60* homestead valuation and prebate forms right here."

"No good," came the reply, followed by ominous notations on the clipboard. The officer glanced over at the kitchen table. "Reading some *conventional* seed catalogs? Don't you know about the requirement to use only *organic* seeds?"

"But that's just for varieties that are commercially available," I whined. "And besides, I haven't even *bought* any seeds yet. I'm just browsing. That's not against the rules, is it?"

"Maybe not, but impure thoughts are the first step to impure foods. I'm afraid you'll have to come downtown for a hearing before an organic jury of your peers."

He slapped a pair of handcuffs on me and began to lead me out to the organic paddy wagon—a 1967 Volkswagen bus with a lava lamp on the roof and USDA's organic seal on its front doors.

"Okay, okay, take it easy," I said. "I'll *stop* selling vegetables as organic. I'll call them local, or authentic, maybe pesticide-free, or just, uh, grown with love and tenderness."

He stopped abruptly and uncuffed me. "Very well, but see that you do. Just remember, no more *o* word. I'll be watching."

---

*Act 60 is Vermont's rather complex mechanism for assessing school taxes.—Ed.

School Lunches and
Chicken Nuggets

Behold the chicken nugget, Nature's perfect food.

Son number one informs me, "They're golden brown, bite-sized, crunchy on the outside, and chewy on the inside!"

Son number two asks, "Daddy, what are chicken nuggets made of?"

"Well, chicken I suppose, I mean…I hope. Let's look it up." We surf the Internet. "Yup, says right here, chicken patties—wow, 16 grams of fat per serving."

"Don't be so negative, Dad. They serve them at school a lot, and they taste good."

"If they called them pulverized poultry pellets would you still eat them?"

"Gross! Why do grown-ups have to wreck everything?"

And so concludes today's nutrition lesson.

Helping kids eat well is easy during the first few years, when parents have at least some control over what goes in their children's mouths, notwithstanding all those miscellaneous household objects kids always chew on. After that, though, it's birthday parties, meals with friends, and—perhaps the scariest eating experience of all—school lunches.

At home, we try to eat healthy food: fresh local vegetables, whole grains, no artificial stuff. But weekday lunches are out of our control, and include hot dogs, fries, canned fruit, and, yes, chicken nuggets. What's a granola-lovin', tofu-totin' dad to do?

Well, I don't blame the schools, because they're trying hard with the money they have. The 47,000 school lunches served every day in Vermont cost an average of $2.15 apiece, and only 42 percent of that is for food. What kind of a lunch can *you* make for a buck? These cheap lunches are due in part to the national school lunch program's low reimbursement rate to schools, and to nutritional requirements that don't emphasize freshness or quality.

Meanwhile, trends in child health are alarming. Obesity, Type 2 diabetes, and other disorders linked to bad eating habits are on the rise. Obviously, school lunches aren't the only cause; television ads promote junk food, fast food restaurants serve it, and busy lifestyles discourage home cooking.

Something needs to be done. Fortunately, there's a growing interest in farm-to-school programs, which specifically aim to improve child nutrition while enhancing local markets for farmers. They work best when linked to a classroom curriculum that helps kids connect to where their food comes from. In Vermont, we have FEED: Food Education Every Day, a program developed by the Northeast Organic Farming Association of Vermont. So far they've worked with four schools to show that local food can be brought into cafeterias and classrooms. The USDA also has a fledgling program aimed at connecting farms and schools. But communities don't need a program to help them start addressing this issue. Parents and school boards can work with cooks and food vendors to encourage the use of local food, and they can also look for a little more money per meal if that's what it takes. It's a win-win investment. Healthier kids, healthier farms. They go together like soup and a sandwich.

John Deere

John Deere, the inventor of the self-polishing steel plow, was born in Rutland in 1804. Inventing a plow may not sound all that impressive, since people have been pushing them since time immemorial, but Deere's refinement of the cast-iron plow played a big role in the settling of the West and the conversion of millions of acres of prairie into productive agricultural land.

At seventeen, John Deere began his career as a blacksmith, apprenticing in Middlebury, Vermont. He later worked in Burlington and Vergennes, and eventually started his own business in Leicester. After his smithy was hit by lightning and subsequently burned, Deere moved to Royalton and then Hancock; there, he made highly polished pitchforks and shovels that were in steady demand throughout western Vermont. But while he was a fine blacksmith, he wasn't the best of all possible businessmen, and he was chronically in debt. In 1836, like many others Vermonters, he headed west to seek a better future.

He set out with a few tools and, after weeks of travel by boat and stagecoach, he reached the small village of Grand Detour, Illinois, which had been settled by Leonard Andrus, another Vermonter. The need for a blacksmith was so great there that, two days after he arrived, he built a forge and began serving the locals: Horses needed shoes and plows needed repair, and the pioneers he did work for frequently complained to Deere that plowing was slow and laborious. The problem, they said, was that the rich prairie soil clung to the cast-iron plows they had brought from the East, and they had to stop frequently and scrape it off.

Deere was a creative fellow, and he thought about what could be done. In 1837, during a visit to a nearby sawmill, a flash of light from a broken saw blade caught his eye, and he got an idea. Using that broken saw blade, John Deere fashioned a steel plow with a highly polished surface that scoured itself as it turned the soil. It was such a success that Deere went into the business of manufacturing plows. News of John Deere's self-polishing plow spread quickly, and by 1842 he was selling a hundred a year.

But running a business on the frontier wasn't easy: There were few banks, poor transportation, and a scarcity of steel, and this meant that Deere's first plows were made from whatever pieces of steel he could find. To address this problem, he ordered special rolled steel all the way from England in 1843.

Three years later, the first slab of plow steel ever rolled in the United States was made in Pittsburgh and shipped to Moline, Illinois, where it was used in the factory Deere had opened there to take advantage of water power and transportation offered by the Mississippi River. Ten years after making his first plow, John Deere produced 1,000 plows a year and, by 1855, he was selling 13,000 plows a year. He was always tinkering with the design because, as he said, "If we don't improve our product, somebody else will." The corporation he formed in 1868, Deere and Company, eventually became one of the largest manufacturers of agricultural equipment in the world.

A Fable for Consumers

Once upon a time, not so very far away, there was a place that was blessed with many good things. The water was clean and abundant, the soils were deep and fertile, and the climate was suitable for growing plants and raising animals. People came from near and far to settle this place, and they learned to live together and look out for each other, for the most part. There was much hard work and perseverance and the people prospered, for the most part. Fields were cleared, farms were established, and forests were harvested. The people learned about working with the soil, the seasons, and the cycles of life.

Over time, an abundance came from the land, and the wealth and power of the people grew and grew. As the generations passed, the goal of the people changed from survival to subsistence to comfort, and, finally, to consumption. The people were good, but they had a fondness for trinkets and gadgets that just wouldn't quit.

And it came to pass that the people were so efficient and so productive that only a few of them were needed to meet the population's basic needs. So the farmers and the foresters and the fishermen became a small minority, and the majority of the people knew not and cared not how their basic needs were being met. They were too busy producing, distributing, and marketing trinkets and gadgets.

In time, the diversity and quantity of trinkets and gadgets came to reach astounding proportions. They came in every size and shape, in every color, and they made all manner of sounds and light, with assembly sometimes, but not always, required. Even the basic needs of life became a merchandising target, so that food, shelter, clothing, and reproduction were soon accessorized.

The demand for trinkets, gadgets, and accessories was so strong, and the people's desire for new products so insatiable, that disposability became widespread, to make room for new stuff. And as the people became more and more obsessed with the making and using of stuff, they decided to measure their success in that manner. They constantly measured how much stuff they were using. They felt good when lots of stuff was produced and consumed, and they worried when less stuff was. Their goal became continuous growth and consumption. To meet this goal, they set out upon the land, and they toiled to transform it. They covered it with roadways for moving stuff here and there, and they built many big boxes for keeping stuff in. There were never enough roads, and never enough boxes, and never enough big holes in the ground where the people could throw away their old stuff.

Now there were some people who spoke of the consequences of neverending consumption, and of the need to care for the resources that generated the stuff. These folks didn't sell a lot of product or enhance quarterly profits, so they were tolerated but largely ignored. But one day the people began to notice that they were running out of things they valued just as much, if not more, than trinkets and gadgets. But they had taken these things for granted, like clean water, clean air, good farmland, and aesthetically pleasing places to live.

So the people set out to change their ways, and to find more satisfaction in nonmaterial things. They built a new economy based on maintenance rather than growth, and they found that they could make stuff that lasted a long time, and was still fun to consume. They learned that they could grow things and build things and move things using technology that protected nature and preserved resources for generations to come. And the people found that they had a lot of free time once they stopped trying to accumulate so much excess wealth to buy so much excess stuff. The people turned their attention to caring for the planet and each other, and they found joy in the building of healthy communities and loving relationships. And they prospered, and were happy ever after.

2003

Raspberries:
Bramble on Rose

The raspberry is one of nature's perfect foods: It's tasty and healthy. There's nothing more mouth-watering than a ripe, fresh-picked raspberry, but this fruit also makes delicious jams and desserts. And, unlike so many other treats, raspberries are little bombshells of health—they contain a lot of vitamin C, plus smaller amounts of a dozen other vitamins and minerals. Recently, raspberries have also been shown to contain ellagic acid, which is a cancer-preventing compound. One cup of raspberries contains nearly four grams of fiber and just sixty-one calories.

The raspberry plant is a member of the rose family, and there are several types of raspberries. Red raspberries are the first to ripen, followed by black and purple raspberries. Red raspberries are more cold-hardy than the other types, and there are more red varieties to choose from. Each variety has its pros and cons.

'Taylor' is the best-tasting, but it is susceptible to diseases. 'Boyne' is the hardiest, but the berries are soft. 'Newburgh' and 'Killarney' are two other varieties hardy enough for Vermont. Purple raspberries are hybrids of red and black raspberries, and have a growth habit similar to black raspberries. Yellow raspberries grow pretty much like red raspberries.

Raspberries are perennial, but individual canes live just two years. The summer-bearing red raspberries that most people are familiar with produce their crop only on two-year-old canes. Newer, ever-bearing varieties can produce a fall crop on their first-year canes, but often these varieties fail to ripen in time to avoid Vermont's early fall frosts.

The red raspberry is indigenous to both Asia Minor and North America. The Romans may have been the first to domesticate the raspberry, as early as the fourth century. In medieval times wild berries were used for food and medicine, and the juice was used for painting. In the thirteenth century King Edward I of England promoted the cultivation of berries, and by the seventeenth century berry bushes were abundant in British gardens.

When European settlers came to America, they found Native Americans already eating wild berries, often drying them for preservation and ease of transportation. The first commercial raspberry nursery in the U.S. started selling plants imported from Europe in 1771, and by 1867 over forty different varieties were known. After the Civil War, major production areas were developed, and by 1880 approximately 2,000 acres were in cultivation. By 1919, production had risen to 54,000 acres, peaking at around 60,000 acres in midcentury.

Today, with improved varieties and horticultural practices, raspberry production is more intensive than in the past. Yields now average over three tons per acre nationwide. The leading red raspberry growing areas are Washington, Oregon, and California, and most of this production is for processing.

In New England, freshly harvested raspberries are an important crop for pick-your-own farms and retail stands that sell the highest-quality produce directly to the consumer.

Potatoes
Past and Present

We've eaten them boiled. We've eaten them mashed. We've eaten them baked and scalloped and hashed.

Apologies to Dr. Seuss, but when it comes to potatoes, we do eat a lot. Worldwide, the potato is a major food crop, exceeded only by wheat, rice, and corn. On average, Americans eat 140 pounds of spuds annually, mostly in processed form like fries and chips. But the potato is more than just popular; it's also immortal. Imagine—a vegetable that never dies. This is because the potato is vegetatively propagated: Each new plant comes from a piece of an older plant. All potatoes sprout from the eyes of some other potato.

The new plants that appear each spring are clones of their parents, harvested the previous autumn, and their parents were derived from the harvest before that. Which came from potatoes from a previous year, and so on, and so on. Thus their claim to immortality.

Botanically, potatoes are tubers, which are found below ground but are not part of the plant's root system. Instead, they are fleshy swellings on underground stems, called stolons. And while most of the flowers produced by commercial potato varieties are sterile, occasionally they will reproduce in the conventional fashion, resulting in the true seed that is so dear to potato plant breeders.

The most famous of these breeders was Luther Burbank. In 1872, while walking in his garden outside of Lancaster, Massachusetts, Burbank found one of these rare seed balls ripening on an 'Early Rose' potato plant. This potato fruit contained twenty-three tiny seeds that Burbank planted, then selecting two plants from the seedlings. Later, when Burbank described the launching of his career, he said, "It was from the potatoes of those two plants—carefully raised, carefully dug, jealously guarded, and painstakingly planted the next year—that I built the 'Burbank' potato. And it was from the Burbank potato that I made my beginning as a plant developer." The Burbank potato was the ancestor of the 'Russet Burbank,' now the most widely grown variety in the United States, and the source of most of our french fries.

The Inca people of South America were the first to cultivate potatoes several thousand years ago. Europeans discovered the potato much later when the Spanish conquered what is now Peru and, by the end of the sixteenth century, families of Basque sailors had begun to cultivate potatoes along the coast of northern Spain. Half a century later Sir Walter Raleigh introduced potatoes to Ireland, planting them on land given to him by Queen Elizabeth I. Two hundred and fifty years later, the potato had become the primary food of the Irish population Then, in 1845 and 1846, the fungus that causes late blight destroyed the potato crop and caused the Irish Potato Famine. A million people died and a million more left the country.

Although potatoes had arrived in the Colonies in 1621, along with all the other vegetables delivered to Jamestown, the first permanent potato plantings in North America were not established until a full hundred years later near Londonderry, New Hampshire. The spuds that were planted had come from Ireland, and the name *Irish potato* has stuck ever since.

Diversity in Dairying

Dairy farmers are facing tough times, in Vermont and across the country. The price they're getting for their milk is low—so low that it doesn't cover their costs of production. How would you feel if you lost money every day you went to work? It's no wonder that so many farmers decide to stop doing what they love to do, what they've done all their lives.

As one farmer said, "When I started out 25 years ago, a shovel cost $13. Now it's $50. But the price of milk hasn't changed much."

In the early '70s Vermont had 4,000 dairy farms with an average of fifty cows that each produced 10,000 pounds of milk a year. Today, the average cow produces almost twice as much, and the average farm has twice as many cows. Since consumption of milk isn't rising, it's no wonder we're down to 1,400 dairy farms. And although Vermont makes almost three billion pounds of milk a year, that's less than 2 percent of the national total. A lot of other states are good at making milk, too.

Meanwhile, many local processors and distributors have been bought up or have gone under. It's called consolidation, and the dairy industry has plenty of company in that, from automobiles to poultry to department stores.

So who cares if our dairy farms disappear? There's plenty of milk in the supermarket. Get over it.

Well, there's one little hitch: Dairy farms provide Vermont with a lot more than milk. They are the key to our remarkable landscape. They provide places to snowmobile, hunt, and hike. and they're a bulwark against sprawl, helping to maintain our small-town-and-village settlement pattern. All this brings in billions of dollars, both in tourism and economic development, as entrepreneurs and corporations seek out Vermont for its quality of life.

So what can we do? From the experts, farmers, and politicians you hear some very different ideas, some of them contradictory and many of them right. We need to hedge our bets as milk prices rise and fall by promoting dairy farms of all types.

We need to support a diversity of farms, including small ones that add value to their milk by bottling it or making cheese or yogurt, organic farms that get a higher price for milk by meeting strict stewardship standards, and grass-based farms that avoid the expense of growing corn. And yes, large farms that aim to reduce their costs of production.

Large farms have to be situated where local communities want them, and they must be thoughtfully regulated to assure protection of our natural resources. Organic farms have to be careful not to grow too fast, flooding the market and lowering prices, putting them in the same boat as conventional farms. And organic farms need protection from genetically engineered crops that could threaten their organic certification.

Farms that make value-added products like cheese need continued support from state agencies and the university to assure they achieve the highest quality. And they need consumers to recognize and buy these products at a premium.

One size doesn't fit all—so let's celebrate diversity in dairy farming.

Herding Cats and
Coaching Soccer

If you like herding cats, then try coaching first grade soccer. I do, and it's not as easy as I thought it would be. Of course, I'm not especially qualified, but I do meet the minimum requirements. I'm ambulatory, I'm good at yelling, and ... I have a whistle. So I was drafted when I arrived with my son to sign up for the local recreational league.

No problem, I thought. *We'll dribble, we'll pass, we'll score, right? Most of all, we'll have fun.*

"Okay, team," I said, "it's not about who wins or loses. We're here to have *fun*."

"Daddy," my son says with the exasperation of an all-knowing seven-year-old, "it's way more fun when you win."

So, to prepare for victory, we practice. Dribbling, passing, trapping—all interspersed with fits of jumping all over each another, emergency bathroom breaks, and round robins of "I'm thirsty. When can I get a drink?"

Then comes game time.

"Let's assign positions. Jeff, you play goalie."

"*I* want to play goalie."

"No, *I* want to play goalie."

"No, *I* do."

"He played last time. It's *my* turn."

"Whoa, whoa," I said. "You'll all get to play goalie. What's the big deal with goalie, anyway?"

"Well," pipes up one youngster, wise beyond his years, "you don't have to do much, but it's really important."

Finally the teams are positioned and the game starts. "Spread out," I yell. "Pass," I yell. Then again: "Spread out. Pass. Pass. Spread *out*." You get the idea. I think beekeepers would make good first-grade soccer coaches. They know how to manage a swarm.

Suddenly the ball squirts free of the crowd. It surprises an unsuspecting player who's been contemplating his navel, or perhaps talking to the crickets in the grass. He jumps to attention, gives the ball a mighty kick, and runs ahead of the crowd. It looks like a breakaway goal.

"The other way!" I scream. "We're going the other way!" Luckily, one of our fastest players intercepts him. Then he trips and falls. I blow the whistle and run over, adrenaline pumping because I can't tell how seriously the child is injured. He's crumpled on the ground, tears flowing.

"Are you okay? Does it hurt?"

He just sobs.

"Where does it hurt?"

"It doesn't," he sobs, "but I got my new soccer shirt all dirty!" Then quick as wink he's up and over it, even if coach isn't.

Soon the ball goes out of bounds. I blow the whistle, declaring a corner kick. It's just my luck that a parent on the sidelines actually knows the rules. "*Goalie* kick," she corrects me. "Are you teaching them the game or just having fun?"

"Hey, if they go in the right direction, I'm happy," I mumble.

There's a minute left; the score is tied. We prepare for the kick, and play is about to resume when I see my left forward waving frantically. I jog over.

"What's the problem?" I ask.

"I'm really glad the game's almost over," my left forward confides. "My mom has cookies for me when we are done."

Play on.

The Food Odometer

There was something special on the menu at Smoke Jack's restaurant in Burlington. And 150 miles away in Brattleboro, there it was again, on the menu of the Riverview Cafe. It was the names of local farms, and you'll find these menu mentions at dozens of fine eateries that belong to the Vermont Fresh Network, an organization dedicated to connecting farmers and chefs. This effort to put locally grown food on the menu often does so, literally, and when a restaurant actually prints the names of farms along with their descriptions of a grilled chicken sandwich or a cheese plate, it's more than just waxing poetic about agriculture. It's bringing your attention to the fact that the ingredients are of superior quality.

You can taste the quality in the chicken from Misty Knoll Farm in New Haven. Unlike run-of-the-mill birds from most poultry producers that never run free because they are confined to cages, the birds at Misty Knoll are allowed to move about in open spaces.

You can see and hear the quality in the crisp salad greens from Lilac Ridge Farm in West Brattleboro, picked that morning and delivered within hours. According to Tristan Toleno, owner and chef at the Riverview, "I buy all my chicken from Misty Knoll Farm, because it's a better product from a culinary point of view, and the salad greens I get from Lilac Ridge Farm are fresher than anything I could buy wholesale. But the truth is that purchasing this way costs me a little bit more, so it's important that my customers recognize and appreciate the use of local products."

Supporting businesses that buy from local farms also helps the Vermont economy. The $500 million that Vermont farmers gross every year is the basis for several billion dollars of economic activity in our communities.

And buying local has another important advantage that's not often recognized: It saves gas. That conclusion was reached by researchers at Iowa State University who recently published a report called, "Checking the food odometer: how far does your food travel?" In it, they analyzed the distance that sixteen produce items traveled when thirty-four different farms sold them to conference centers, hotels, and other institutions in Central Iowa. Then they compared these distances to a conservative estimate of travel for the same produce items that arrived by truck at Chicago and St. Louis terminal markets.

They found that the local produce traveled an average of fifty-six miles, while the produce from conventional sources had come nearly 1,500 miles. And this study dealt only with domestic produce. If you consider that 39 percent of the fruit and 12 percent of the vegetables we eat come from outside the United States, the numbers would have been even more compelling.

So eat well, support Vermont's agriculture, and save energy by buying local.

Nonprofits in Vermont

This may sound funny, but nonprofit organizations are big business in Vermont. That's according to a report published by the Vermont Alliance of Nonprofit Organizations called "Not the Non-Sector: The Facts about the Charitable Nonprofit Community in Vermont." The report is based on research conducted in collaboration with the University of Vermont Center for Rural Studies. Here's what it says: Vermont ranks tops in the nation in number of nonprofits per capita. There are nearly 2,700 charitable nonprofits in the state.

These organizations generate $2.8 billion in revenues, almost 11 percent of the gross state product. Nonprofits are also the source of 42,000 jobs, or 12 percent of all employment.

In Vermont, nonprofit corporations are formed for mutual benefit or public benefit. Mutual benefit corporations, such as clubs, benefit their members. Public benefit corporations serve a larger community good.

Contrary to the impression given by the name, nonprofits can earn a profit. But that profit, or surplus funds, must be used to support the work of the organization. In traditional businesses, where corporations are formed to benefit owners or shareholders, profit is the ultimate measure of success. In the nonprofit world, the measure of success is fulfillment of a public purpose, like education, health care, or environmental protection.

Vermont's nonprofits are very diverse. Most people would recognize that hospitals and religious congregations are nonprofits, but they may not be aware that their local child-care center, community theater, rescue squad, humane society, and outdoor education center may also be nonprofits. A variety of advocacy groups from across the political spectrum are also nonprofits, as are groups that provide affordable housing, social services, and support for the arts. Philanthropic foundations are part of Vermont's nonprofit community, too; in most cases the foundations serve as funding sources for the smaller nonprofits that deliver services.

The majority of Vermont's nonprofit organizations are small. About two-thirds of them have annual revenues of less than $200,000 a year, and half of those have revenues of less than $25,000.

Vermonters generously support nonprofit charitable organizations in two critical ways: with time and with money. About a third of Vermont's charitable organizations rely entirely on volunteer work, and many others could not survive without significant volunteer labor. So it's a good thing that we're eager to volunteer, and better still that we do it in fairly large numbers—about 59 percent of Vermonters volunteer, as compared to 44 percent nationally. About 85 percent of us also make the financial donations upon which many of Vermont's nonprofits depend, since more than a third of their revenue comes from private sources. Overall, Vermont taxpayers donate about 2.5 percent of their income to charities, but this is an area that could use some improvement. The national average is 3 percent of income.

Supporting nonprofits makes sense, since their impact can be felt in every community and every profession. They provide a structure for Vermonters to work together to solve problems, and they complement the activities of business and government, adding a dimension to community life that makes Vermont so special.

Peanut Butter

October is Peanut Butter Lovers' Month but, for my kids, it's a year-round love affair. While the average American consumes three-and-a-half pounds of peanut butter every year, I bet my children eat ten times that. In fact, my kids eat so much peanut butter they should have been named Skippy and Jif.

How can they eat peanut butter and jelly for lunch every day?

"Boring," I say. But they're committed to this dietary monoculture.

And that's okay, because peanut butter is nutritious. Although high in fats, they're mostly so-called *good* fats that are monounsaturated. No unhealthy trans-fats here. Peanut butter also contains some soluble fiber and a lot of protein.

Ground peanuts have been eaten for centuries in Africa and China, but peanut butter is an American invention. In 1890, Dr. John Kellogg of Michigan started making peanut butter as a vegetarian source of protein for his patients. He and his brother, W.K. Kellogg, patented a process of preparing nut meal, described as "a pasty adhesive substance that is for convenience of distinction termed nut butter." Their product didn't taste very good because the peanuts were steamed instead of roasted. Then the Kelloggs turned their attention to cereals, and the rest is history.

Commercial peanut butter was born in 1922, when a process was developed to keep the oil from separating and better packaging kept the product from spoiling. By 1928, the national brands we see on the grocer's shelves started appearing, and peanut butter was on its way to becoming one of the default ingredients in every kid's lunchbox. To be legally labeled *peanut butter*, it must contain 90 percent peanuts. The other 10 percent often includes sugar, salt, and hydrogenated oils. If my kids are going to eat so much of something, I'd just as soon avoid these added ingredients; when they were little, I sneaked the all-natural organic peanut butter right by them. But once they got a whiff of the store stuff, things started to change.

"Look at the label," I'd say. "See, it's got all this stuff in it besides peanuts."

"But it's creamy, and we *like* sugar."

I'm not a food fanatic, but I decided to explore the options with regard to purity, price, and taste. Here's what I found: There's an all-natural peanut butter that sells for two bucks a jar at the supermarket. It's not organic, but it's made only from peanuts and salt. The kids will eat it.

Grind-your-own natural peanut butter at the food co-op is about the same price, but the texture is mealy. "Sorry Dad. No way."

We tried a different organic brand at about $3.50 a jar from the co-op, $3 in the bulk section. Very smooth, with good flavor. "But there's *brown* stuff in it!"

"That's the natural skin of the peanut," I explained.

"Gross!" they replied.

Then another organic brand—creamy, smooth, and free of the brown stuff—went on sale for $2.69 at the co-op. It was the answer to their objections and my peanut dreams, so I ordered two cases. At the bulk price, and with my working-member discount, it cost just over $2 a jar. Victory at last.

"Uh, Dad? I'm getting kind of sick of peanut butter. Can I have bologna for lunch instead?"

Climate Change

It's really too much to handle—too big, too scary. So we ignore it, deny it, or make jokes about oceanfront property in Vermont. It's climate change.

Some call it global warming, but it's more like planetary transformation. In addition to higher temperature, precipitation patterns are changing, oceans are rising, ice is melting, and plants and animals are adapting.

The enormity of it hit me at a conference on climate and horticulture. Oh, well, you might think, a gathering of alarmists. I don't think so. There were scientists from Cornell, Tufts, the USDA, and a dozen universities, all saying with complete unanimity that the question isn't whether there *is* climate change, but *how much*. The good news is that we can influence the answer.

Climatology predicts change over many decades, and is not like weather forecasting, where long-term predictions mean the five-day outlook. But by using weather-station data collected over the past century, climatologists at the University of New Hampshire have determined that the average annual temperature in the Northeast has risen by 1.8 degrees.

That little change is powerful: The frost-free growing season is a week longer; lake ice breaks up five days sooner; and Vermont's maple syrup production, which tends to be greater in years with colder temperatures, is declining. That's not solely due to climate change, but if temperatures continue to rise, sugar maples may not survive in New England. New insect pests will arrive, and cool-season crops will no longer thrive.

The main culprit behind climate change is human activity that generates carbon dioxide, primarily by burning fossil fuel. In the U.S., we lead the world by generating over five tons of CO_2 per person per year. Scientists who study atmospheric CO_2 find that, after centuries of stability, it has risen by a third in the past hundred years. What's scary is that fuel consumption shows no signs of slowing down, and places like China are just getting started.

Predicting climate is complicated. Scientific models must factor in all the gases we put in the air as well as the effects of natural forces. They must consider how much carbon is absorbed as plants grow. There are many different climate models and they all generate what are basically educated guesses. But none of these guesses is reassuring: The Earth is getting warmer, and fast.

How can we slow down these big changes? First, we've got to recognize that just a decrease of a few degrees is important; those few degrees will mean a lot less environmental change. Second, we have to put knowledge to work to help us be more efficient and less consumptive in our technology and lifestyle.

But, ultimately, we need more long-term greed. If we were greedier for profit, comfort, and stability for the next generation, not just today, we'd make better decisions. We'd also be greedy about wanting to hang on to habitats, greedy to keep the plant and animal species we know, and greedy for a healthy planet for our children's children.